D1546169

6.50 EC
NO

ASTRONOMICAL LORE IN CHAUCER

BY

FLORENCE M. GRIMM

AMS PRESS
NEW YORK

235774

Reprinted from the edition of 1919, Lincoln
First AMS EDITION published 1970
Manufactured in the United States of America

International Standard Book Number: 0-404-02919-1

Library of Congress Card Catalog Number: 70-128992

AMS PRESS, INC.
NEW YORK, N.Y. 10003

CONTENTS

ASTRONOMICAL LORE IN CHAUCER

I

ASTRONOMY IN THE MIDDLE AGES

The conspicuousness of astronomical lore in the poetry of Chaucer is due to its importance in the life of his century. In the mediaeval period, astronomy (or 'astrology,' for the two names were used indifferently to cover the same subject) was one of the vital interests of men. The ordinary man of the Middle Ages knew much more than do most men to-day about the phenomena of the heavens; conveniences such as clocks, almanacs, and charts representing celestial phenomena were rare, and direct observations of the apparent movements and the relative positions of the heavenly bodies were necessary for the regulation of man's daily occupations. Furthermore, the belief in a geocentric system of the universe, which in Chaucer's century was almost universally accepted, was of vast significance in man's way of thinking. Accepting this view, all the heavenly bodies seemed to have been created for the sole benefit of man, inhabiting the central position in the universe; their movements, always with reference to the earth as a center, brought to man light, heat, changes of season—all the conditions that made human life possible on the earth.

Not only did the man of the Middle Ages see in the regular movements of the celestial spheres the instruments by which God granted him physical existence, but in the various aspects of heavenly phenomena he saw the governing principles of his moral life. The arrangement of the heavenly bodies with regard to one another at various times was supposed to exert undoubted power over the course of terrestrial events. Each planet was thought to have special attributes and a special influence over men's lives. Venus was the planet of love, Mars, of war and hostility, the sun, of power and honor, and so forth. Each was mysteriously connected with a certain color, with a metal, too, the alchemists said, and each had special power over some organ of the human body. The planet's influence was believed to vary greatly according to its position in the heavens, so that to determine a man's destiny accurately it was necessary to consider the aspect of the whole heavens, especially at the moment of his birth, but also at other times. This was called "casting the horoscope" and was regarded as of great importance in enabling a man to guard against threatening perils or bad tendencies, and to make the best use of favorable opportunities.

It is not astonishing, then, that the great monuments of literature in the mediaeval period and even much later are filled with astronomical and astrological allusions; for these are but reflections of vital human interests of the times. The greatest poetical work of the Middle Ages, Dante's *Divina Commedia*, is rich in astronomical lore, and its dramatic action is projected against a cosmographical background reflecting the view of Dante's contemporaries as to the structure of the world. Milton, writing in the seventeenth century, bases the cosmology of his *Paradise Lost* in the main on the Ptolemaic system, but makes Adam and the archangel Raphael discuss the relative merits of this system and the heliocentric view of the universe. The latter had been brought forth by Copernicus a century earlier, but even in Milton's day had not yet succeeded in supplanting the old geocentric cosmology.

The view of the universe which we find reflected in Chaucer's poetry is chiefly based on the Ptolemaic system of astronomy, though it shows traces of very much more primitive cosmological ideas. The Ptolemaic system owes its name to the famous Alexandrian astronomer of the second century A. D., Claudius Ptolemy, but is based largely on the works and discoveries of the earlier Greek philosophers and astronomers, especially Eudoxus, Hipparchus, and Aristarchus, whose investigations Ptolemy compiled and, along some lines, extended. Ptolemaic astronomy was a purely geometrical or mathematical system which represented the observed movements and relative positions of the heavenly bodies so accurately that calculations as to their positions at any given time could be based upon it. Ptolemy agreed with his contemporaries in the opinion that to assign causes for the celestial movements was outside the sphere of the astronomer. This was a proper field of philosophy; and the decisions of philosophers, especially those of Aristotle, were regarded as final, and their teaching as the basis upon which observed phenomena should be described.

According to the Ptolemaic system the earth is a motionless sphere fixed at the center of the universe. It can have no motion, for there must be some fixed point in the universe to which all the motions of the heavenly bodies may be referred; if the earth had motion, it was argued, this would be proportionate to the great mass of the earth and would cause objects and animals to fly off into the air and be left behind. Ptolemy believed this reason sufficient to make untenable the idea of a rotatory motion of the earth, although he was fully aware that to suppose such a motion of the earth would simplify exceedingly the representations of the celestial movements. It did not occur to him that to suppose the earth's atmosphere to participate in its motion would obviate this difficulty. The earth was but a point in comparison with the immense sphere to which the stars were attached and which revolved about the earth once in every twenty-four hours, imparting its motion to sun, moon, and planets, thus causing day and night and the rising and setting of the heavenly bodies. The irregular motions of the planets were accounted for by supposing them to move on circles of small spheres called 'epicycles', the centres of which moved around the 'deferents', or circles of large spheres which carried the planets in courses concentric to the star sphere. By giving each of the planets an epicycle and deferent of the proper relative size and velocity the varied oscillations of the planets, as far as they could be followed by means of the simple instruments then in use, were almost perfectly accounted for.

Though it was a purely mathematical system which only attempted to give a basis for computing celestial motions, Ptolemaic astronomy is of great importance historically as it remained the foundation of theoretical astronomy for more than 1400 years. Throughout the long dark centuries of the Middle Ages it survived in the studies of the retired students of the monasteries and of the few exceptionally enlightened men who still had some regard for pagan learning in the days when many of the Church Fathers denounced it as heretical.

Ptolemy was the last of the great original Greek astronomers. The Alexandrian school produced, after him, only copyists and commentators, and the theoretical astronomy of the Greeks, so highly perfected in Ptolemy's *Almagest*, was for many centuries almost entirely neglected. The Roman State gave no encouragement to the study of theoretical astronomy and produced no new school of astronomy. Although it was the fashion for a Roman to have a smattering of Greek astronomy, and famous Latin authors like Cicero, Seneca, Strabo and Pliny wrote on astronomy, yet the Romans cared little for original investigations and contributed nothing new to the science. The Romans, however, appreciated the value of astronomy in measuring time, and applied to the Alexandrian school to satisfy their practical need for a calendar. What Julius Caesar obtained from the Alexandrian Sosigenes, he greatly improved and gave to the Empire, as the calendar which, with the exception of the slight change made by Gregory XIII, we still use.

The pseudo-astronomical science of astrology, or the so-called 'judicial astronomy' was pursued during the Roman Empire and throughout the Middle Ages with much greater zeal than theoretical astronomy. The interest in astrology, to be sure, encouraged the study of observational astronomy to a certain extent; for the casting of horoscopes to foretell destinies required that the heavenly bodies be observed and methods of calculating their positions at any time or place be known. But there was no desire to inquire into the underlying laws of the celestial motions or to investigate the real nature of the heavenly phenomena.

If the Roman State did not encourage astronomy, the Roman Church positively discouraged it. The Bible became and long remained the sole authority recognized by the Church Fathers as to the constitution of the universe. By many of the Patristics Ptolemaic astronomy was despised; not because it did not describe accurately the observed phenomena of the heavens, for it did this in a way that could scarcely have been improved upon with the facilities for observation then available; and not because it was founded upon the false assumption that the earth is the motionless center of the universe about which all heavenly bodies revolve; but because there was no authority in Scripture for such a system, and it could not possibly be made consistent with the cosmology of Genesis. Allegorical descriptions of the universe based on the Scriptures held almost complete sway over the mediaeval mind. The whole universe was represented allegorically by the tabernacle and its furniture. The earth was flat and rectangular like the table of shew bread, and surrounded on all four sides by the ocean. The walls of heaven beyond this supported the firmament shaped like a half-cylinder. Angels moved the sun, moon, and stars across the firmament and let down rain through its windows from the expanse of water above.

By no means all of the early Church Fathers were wholly without appreciation of the fruits of Greek astronomical science. Origen and Clement of Alexandria, while believing in the scriptural allegories, tried to reconcile them with the results of pagan learning. In the West, Ambrose of Milan and later Augustine, were at least not opposed to the idea of the earth's sphericity, and of the existence of antipodes, although they could not get away from the queer notion of the waters above the firmament. A few enlightened students like Philoponus of Alexandria, Isidore of Seville, the Venerable Bede, and Irish scholars like Fergil and Dicuil, studied the Greek philosophers and accepted some of the pagan scientific teachings.

Fortunately the study of those ancient Latin writers whose works had preserved some of the astronomy of the

Greeks had taken firm root among the patient scholars of the monasteries, and slowly but steadily the geocentric system of cosmology was making its way back into the realm of generally accepted fact, so that by the ninth century it was the system adopted by nearly all scholars.

About the year 1000 began the impetus to learning which culminated in the great revival of the Renaissance. One cause of this intellectual awakening was the contact of Europe with Arab culture through the crusades and through the Saracens in Sicily and the Moors in Spain. The Arabian influence resulted in an increased sense of the importance of astronomy and astrology; for, while the scholars of the Christian world had been devising allegorical representations of the world based on sacred literature, the Arabian scholars had been delving into Greek science, translating Ptolemy and Aristotle, and trying to make improvements upon Ptolemaic astronomy. The spheres of the planets, which Ptolemy had almost certainly regarded as purely symbolical, the Arabs conceived as having concrete existence. This made it necessary to add a ninth sphere to the eight mentioned by Ptolemy; for it was thought sufficient that the eighth sphere should carry the stars and give them their slow movement of precession from west to east. This ninth sphere was the outermost of all and it originated the "prime motion" by communicating to all the inner spheres its diurnal revolution from east to west. In mediaeval astronomy it came to be known as the *primum mobile* or "first movable," while a tenth and motionless sphere was added as the abode of God and redeemed souls. The sun and moon were included among the planets, which revolved about the earth in the order Moon, Mercury, Venus, Sun, Mars, Jupiter, Saturn.

At first the astronomy taught in the universities was based on Latin translations of Arabic commentaries and paraphrases of Aristotle, which had made their way into Aristotle represented in the eyes of most scholastics "the last possibility of wisdom and learning." But by the middle Europe through the Moors in Spain. For several centuries of the thirteenth century Ptolemy began to be rediscovered. The Ptolemaic system of planetary motions was briefly described in a handbook compiled by John Halifax of Holywood, better known as Sacrobosco. Roger Bacon wrote on the spheres, the use of the astrolabe, and astrology, following Ptolemy in his general ideas about the universe. The great mediaeval scholar and philosopher, Thomas Aquinas, was also familiar with the Ptolemaic system; but to most of the men of the thirteenth century Ptolemy's works remained quite unknown. The real revival of Greek astronomy took place in the fourteenth century when scholars began to realize that new work in astronomy must be preceded by a thorough knowledge of the astronomy of the Alexandrian school as exhibited in the *Syntaxis* of Ptolemy. It was then that Greek and Latin manuscripts of works on astronomy began to be eagerly sought for and deciphered, and a firm foundation constructed for the revival of theoretical astronomy.

II

CHAUCER'S SCIENTIFIC KNOWLEDGE

It was in the fourteenth century that Chaucer lived and wrote, and his interest in astronomical lore is, therefore, not surprising. Although the theories of astronomy current in Chaucer's century have been made untenable by the *De Revolutionibus Orbium* of Copernicus, and by Kepler's discovery of the laws of planetary motion; although the inaccurate and unsatisfactory methods of astronomical investigation then in use have been supplanted by the better methods made possible through Galileo's invention of the telescope and through the modern use of spectrum analysis; yet, of all scientific subjects, the astronomy of that period could most nearly lay claim to the name of science according to the present acceptation of the term. For, as we have seen, the interest in astrology during the Middle Ages had fostered the study of observational astronomy, and this

in turn had furnished the science a basis of fact and observation far surpassing in detail and accuracy that of any
other subject.

Practically all of Chaucer's writings contain some reference to the movements and relative positions of the
heavenly bodies, and to their influence on human and mundane affairs, and in some of his works, especially the
treatise on *The Astrolabe,* a very technical and detailed
knowledge of astronomical and astrological lore is displayed.   There is every reason to suppose that, so far as
it satisfied his purposes, Chaucer had made himself familiar
with the whole literature of astronomical science.   His
familiarity with Ptolemaic astronomy is shown in his writings both by specific mention[1] of the name of Ptolemy and his
Syntaxis, commonly known as the 'Almagest,' and by many
more general astronomical references.

Even more convincing evidence of Chaucer's knowledge
of the scientific literature of his time is given in his *Treatise
on the Astrolabe.*   According to Skeat, Part I and at least
two-thirds of Part II are taken, with some expansion and

---

[1]The name of Ptolemy occurs once in *The Somnours Tale* (D. 2289) :

> "As wel as Euclide or (as) Ptholomee."

and once in *The Astrolabe,* I. 17.6:

> "whiche declinacioun, aftur Ptholome, is 23 degrees and 50 minutes, as wel in Cancer as in Capricorne."

The *Almagest* is mentioned in *The Milleres Tale* (A.3208) :

> "His Almageste and bokes grete and smale,"

Twice in *The Wif of Bathes Prologue* occur both the name of the *Almagest* and that of its author:

> " 'Who-so that nil be war by othere men,
> By him shul othere men corrected be.
> The same wordes wryteth Ptholomee;
> Rede in his Almageste, and take it there.' "
>   (D. 180-183)
> "Of alle men y-blessed moot he be,
> The wyse astrologien Dan Ptholome,
> That seith this proverbe in his Almageste,
> 'Of alle men his wisdom is the hyeste,
> That rekketh never who hath the world in honde.' "
>   (D. 323-327)

Professor Lounsbury (*Studies in Chaucer,* ii p. 186 and pp. 396-7)
has difficulty in explaining why Chaucer makes the Wife of Bath
attribute these moral maxims to Ptolemy.   He is inclined to think
that Chaucer, so to   speak, was napping when he put these utter-
ances into the mouth of the Wife of Bath; yet elsewhere he acknow-

alteration, from a work on the Astrolabe by Messahala[1], called, in the Latin translation which Chaucer used, "Compositio et Operatio Astrolabie." This work may have been ultimately derived from a Sanskrit copy, but from Chaucer's own words in the *Prologue to the Astrolabe*[2] it is clear that he made use of the Latin work. The rest of Part II may have been derived from some general compendium of astronomical and astrological knowledge, or from some other of the treatises on the Astrolabe which Chaucer says were common in his time.[3]

Other sources mentioned by Chaucer in *The Astrolabe* are the calendars of John Some and Nicholas Lynne, Carmelite friars who wrote calendars constructed for the meridian of Oxford[4]; and of the Arabian astronomer Abdilazi Alkabucius.[5] In *The Frankeleyns Tale* Chaucer mentions the Tabulae Toletanae,[6] a set of tables composed by order of

---

ledges that the supposition of confused memory on Chaucer's part in this case is hard to reconcile with the knowledge he elsewhere displays of Ptolemy's work. I think it very probable that Chaucer's seeming slip here is deliberate art. The Wife of Bath is one of Chaucer's most humorous creations and the blunders he here attributes to her are quite in keeping with her character. From her fifth husband, who was a professional scholar and a wide reader, she has picked up a store of scattered and incomplete information about books and names, and she loses no opportunity for displaying it. At any rate, whether or not Chaucer had read the *Almagest* in translation, his many cosmological and astronomical references show clearly his acquaintance with the Ptolemaic system of astronomy.

[1]An Arabian scholar of the eighth century.

[2]1.18 ff. "This tretis, divided in fyve parties, wole I shewe thee under ful lighte rewles and naked wordes in English; for Latin ne canstow yit but smal, my lyte sone."

[3]And Lowis, yif so be that I shewe thee in my lighte English as trewe conclusiouns touching this matere, and naught only as trewe but as many and as subtil conclusiouns as ben shewed in Latin in any commune tretis of the Astrolabie, con me the more thank;" *Prologue to the Astrolabe*, 35-39.

[4]Skeat, *Notes on the Astrolabe, Prologue*, 62   "Warton says that 'John Some and Nicholas Lynne' were both Carmelite friars, and wrote calendars constructed for the meridian of Oxford. He adds that Nicholas Lynne is said to have made several voyages to the most northerly parts of the world, charts of which he presented to Edward III. These charts are, however, lost."

[5]*The Astrolabe*, I. 8.9. According to Warton the work in question is an introduction to judicial astronomy. (Lounsbury, II. 398.)

[6]F. 1273. "His tables Toletanes forth he broght,"

Alphonso X, king of Castile, and so called because they were adapted to the city of Toledo.   Works which served Chaucer not as sources of information on scientific subjects but as models for the treatment of astronomical lore in literature were the *De Consolatione Philosophiae* of Boethius, which Chaucer translated and often made use of in his poetry; and the works of Dante, whose influence on Chaucer, probably considerable, has been pointed out by several writers, notably Rambeau[1] who discusses the parallels between *The Hous of Fame* and the *Divina Commedia*.

III

CHAUCER'S COSMOLOGY

Chaucer wrote no poetical work having a cosmographical background as completely set forth as is that in Dante's *Divine Comedy* or that in Milton's *Paradise Lost*. Although his cosmological references are often incidental they are not introduced in a pedantic manner.   Whenever they are not parts of interpolations from other writers his use of them is due to their intimate relation to the life his poetry portrays or to his appreciation of their poetic value.   When Chaucer says, for example, that the sun has grown old and shines in Capricorn with a paler light than is his wont, he is not using a merely conventional device for showing that winter has come, but is expressing this fact in truly poetic manner and in words quite comprehensible to the men of his day, who were accustomed to think of time relations in terms of heavenly phenomena.

Popular   and   scientific   views   of   the   universe   in Chaucer's century were by no means the same.   The untaught man doubtless still thought of the earth as being flat, as it appears to be, as bounded by the waters of the ocean, and as covered by a dome-like material firmament through which the waters above sometimes came as rain;

[1]*Englische Studien* III 209.   See also J. S. P. Tatlock, "Chaucer and Dante," in *Modern Philoloqy*, III, 367. 1905.

while, as we have seen, by the fourteenth century among scholars the geocentric system of astronomy was firmly established and the spheres and epicycles of Ptolemy were becoming more widely known. It is the view held by the educated men of his century that Chaucer's poetry chiefly reflects.

1. *The Celestial Spheres and their Movements*

When we read Chaucer we are transported into a world in which the heavenly bodies and their movements seem to bear a more intimate relation to human life than they do in the world in which we live. The thought of the revolving spheres carrying sun, moon, and planets, regulating light and heat on the earth, and exercising a mysterious influence over terrestrial events and human destiny was a sublime conception and one that naturally appealed to the imagination of a poet. Chaucer was impressed alike by the vastness of the revolving spheres in comparison to the earth's smallness, by their orderly arrangement, and by the unceasing regularity of their appearance which seemed to show that they should eternally abide. In the *Parlement of Foules* he interpolates a passage from Cicero's *Somnium Scipionis* in which Africanus appears to the sleeping Scipio, points out to him the insignificance of our little earth when compared with the vastness of the heavens and then admonishes him to regard the things of this world as of little importance when compared with the joys of the heavenly life to come.[1]

> "Than shewed he him the litel erthe, that heer is,
> At regard of the hevenes quantite;
> And after shewed he him the nyne speres."

The regular arrangement of the planetary spheres clings often to the poet's fancy and he makes many allusions to their order in the heavens. He speaks of Mars as "the thridde hevenes lord above"[2] and of Venus as presiding over

---

[1] *Parlement of Foules*, 57-59.
[2] *Compleynt of Mars*, 29.

the "fifte cercle."[1] In *Troilus and Criseyde* the poet invokes
Venus as the adorning light of the third heaven.[2]

"O blisful light, of which the bemes clere
Adorneth al the thridde hevene faire![3]

Mediaeval astronomers as we have seen, imagined
nine spheres, each of the seven innermost carrying with
it one of the planets in the order mentioned below; the
eighth sphere was that of the fixed stars, and to account for
the precession of the equinoxes, men supposed it to have
a slow motion from west to east, round the axis of the
zodiac; the ninth or outermost sphere they called the
primum mobile, or the sphere of first motion, and supposed
it to revolve daily from east to west, carrying all the other
spheres with it. The thought of the two outer spheres,
the *primum mobile,* whirling along with it all the inner
spheres, and the firmament, bearing hosts of bright stars,
seems to have appealed strongly to the poet's imagination.
In the *Tale of the Man of Lawe* the *primum mobile* is described as crowding and hurling in diurnal revolution from
east to west all the spheres that would naturally follow the
slow course of the zodiac from west to east.[4] Elsewhere the
primum mobile is called the "whele that bereth the sterres"
and is said to turn the heavens with a "ravisshing sweigh:"

"O thou maker of the whele that bereth the sterres,
which that art y-fastned to thy perdurable chayer, and

---

[1] *Lenvoy de Chaucer a Scogan,* 8-12.
"By worde eterne whylom was hit shape
That fro the fifte cercle, in no manere,
Ne mighte a drope of teres doun escape.
But now so wepeth Venus in hir spere,
That with hir teres she wol drenche us here."

[2] Since Chaucer calls Mars the lord of the third heaven and elsewhere speaks of Venus as presiding over that sphere it is evident that
he sometimes reckons from the earth outwards, and sometimes from
the outer sphere of Saturn towards the earth. The regular order
of the planets, counting from the earth, was supposed to be as follows:
Moon, Mercury, Venus, Sun, Mars, Jupiter, Saturn, making Mars the
third from the last.

[3] III. 1-2.

[4]   "O firste moevyng cruel firmament,
With thy diurnal sweigh that crowdest ay
And hurlest al from Est til Occident,
That naturelly wolde holde another way."
(B. 295-8)

tornest the hevene with a ravisshing sweigh, and constrein-
est the sterres to suffren thy lawe;"[1]

The firmament, which in Chaucer is not restricted to
the eighth sphere but generally refers to the whole expanse
of the heavens, is many times mentioned by Chaucer; and
its appearance on clear or cloudy nights, its changing aspects before an impending storm or with the coming of
dawn, beautifully described.[2]

2. *The Harmony of the Spheres*

Some of the cosmological ideas reflected in Chaucer's
writings can be traced back to systems older than the Ptolemaic. The beautiful fancy that the universe is governed
by harmony had its origin in the philosophy of the Pythagoreans in the fourth century B. C., and continued to appeal
to men's imagination until the end of the Middle Ages. It
was thought that the distances of the planetary spheres
from one another correspond to the intervals of a musical
scale and that each sphere as it revolves sounds one note
of the scale. When asked why men could not hear the
celestial harmony, the Pythagoreans said: A blacksmith
is deaf to the continuous, regular beat of the hammers
in his shop; so we are deaf to the music which the spheres
have been sending forth from eternity.

In ancient and mediaeval cosmology it was only the
seven spheres of the planets that were generally supposed
to participate in this celestial music; but the poets have

Chaucer does not use the term 'firmament' with sole reference
to the star-sphere. Here it clearly refers to the *primum mobile*; it
often applies to the whole expanse of the heavens.

[1]*Boethius*, Book I: Metre V, 1-4. The conception of God as
the creator and unmoved mover of the universe originated in the
philosophy of Aristotle, who was the one great authority, aside from
Scripture and the Church Fathers, recognized by the Middle Ages.
God's abode was thought to be in the Empyrean, the motionless sphere
beyond the ninth, and the last heaven. This is the meaning in the
reference to the eternal throne ("perdurable chayer") of God.

[2]Many of these beautiful descriptions, however, are not strictly
Chaucer's own, since they occur in his translation of Boethius. It will
suffice to quote one of these descriptions:

taken liberties with this idea and have given it to us in forms suiting their own fancies. Milton bids all the celestial spheres join in the heavenly melody:

> "Ring out, ye crystal spheres,
> Once bless our human ears,
>   If ye have power to touch our senses so;
> And let your silver chime
> Move in melodious time,
>   And let the base of heaven's deep organ blow;
> And with your ninefold harmony,
> Make up full consort to the angelic symphony."[1]

Shakespeare lets every orb of the heavens send forth its note as it moves:

> "There's not the smallest orb which thou behold'st
> But in his motion like an angel sings,
> Still quiring to the young-eyed cherubins;"[2]

Chaucer, too, makes all nine spheres participate:

> "And after that the melodye herde he
> That cometh of thilke speres thryes three,
> That welle is of musyke and melodye
> In this world heer, and cause of armonye."[3]

Only in unusual circumstances can the music of the spheres be heard by mortal ears. In the lines just quoted the celestial melody is heard during a dream or vision. In *Troilus and Criseyde*, after Troilus' death his spirit is borne aloft to heaven whence he beholds the celestial orbs and hears the melody sent forth as they revolve:

"And, right by ensaumple as the sonne is hid whan the sterres ben clustred (*that is to seyn, whan sterres ben covered with cloudes*) by a swifte winde that highte Chorus, and that the firmament stant derked by wete ploungy cloudes, and that the sterres nat apperen up-on hevene, so that the night semeth sprad up-on erthe: yif thanne the wind that highte Borias, y-sent out of the caves of the contres of Trace, beteth this night (*that is to seyn, chaseth it a-wey*), and descovereth the closed day: than shyneth Phebus y-shaken with sodein light, and smyteth with his bemes in mervelinge eyen." (*Boethius*, Book I: Metre III. 3-12.)

[1]*Hymn on the Nativity*, XIII.
[2]*The Merchant of Venice*, Act. V. Sc. i.
[3]*Parlement of Foules*, 60-63.

"And ther he saugh, with ful avysement,
The erratik sterres, herkeninge armonye
With sownes fulle of hevenish melodye.[1]

3. The Cardinal Points and the Regions of the World

More primitive in origin than the harmony of the spheres are references to the four elements, to the divisions of the world, and to the cardinal points or quarters of the earth. Of these, probably the most primitive is the last. The idea of four cardinal points, the "before," the "behind," the "right," and the "left," later given the names North, South, East, and West, appears among peoples in their very earliest stages of civilization, and because of its great usefulness has remained and probably will remain throughout the history of the human race. Only one of Chaucer's many references to the cardinal points need be mentioned. In the *Man of Lawes Tale* (B.491ff.) the cardinal points are first suggested by an allusion to the four 'spirits of tempest,' which were supposed to have their respective abodes in the four quarters of earth, and then specifically named in the lines following:

"Who bad the foure spirits of tempest,
That power han tanoyen land and see,
'Bothe north and south, and also west and est,
Anoyeth neither see, ne land, ne tree?' "

Of almost equal antiquity are ideas of the universe as a threefold world having heaven above, earth below, and a region of darkness and gloom beneath the earth. Chaucer usually speaks of the threefold world, the "tryne compas," as comprising heaven, earth and sea. Thus in the *Knightes Tale*:[2]

" 'O chaste goddesse of the wodes grene,
To whom bothe hevene and erthe and see is sene,
Quene of the regne of Pluto derk and lowe,' "

---

[1] *Troilus and Criseyde*, V. 1811-1813.
[2] A. 2297-9.

Fame's palace is said to stand midway between heaven, earth and sea:

> "Hir paleys stant, as I shal seye,
> Right even in middes of the weye
> Betwixen hevene, erthe, and see;"[1]

Again in *The Seconde Nonnes Tale,* the name 'tryne compas' is used of the threefold world and the three regions are mentioned:

> "That of the tryne compas lord and gyde is,
> Whom erthe and see and heven, out of relecs,
> Ay herien;"[2]

4.   *Heaven, Hell and Purgatory*

In mediaeval cosmology ideas of heaven, hell, and purgatory, as more or less definitely located regions where the spirts of the dead were either rewarded or punished eternally, or were purged of their earthly sins in hope of future blessedness, play an important part.   According to Dante's poetic conception hell was a conical shaped pit whose apex reached to the center of the earth, purgatory was a mountain on the earth's surface on the summit of which was located the garden of Eden or the earthly paradise, and heaven was a motionless region beyond space and time, the motionless sphere outside of the *primum mobile,* called the Empyrean.

Chaucer's allusions to heaven, hell and purgatory are frequent but chiefly incidental and give no such definite idea of their location as we find in the *Divine Comedy.*   The nearest Chaucer comes to indicating the place of heaven is in *The Parlement of Foules,* 55-6, where Africanus speaks of heaven and then points to the galaxy:

> "And rightful folk shal go, after they dye,
> To heven; and shewed him the galaxye."

---

[1] *Hous of Fame,* ii. 713 ff.
[2] *Seconde Nonnes Tale,* G. 45-47.

Chaucer describes heaven as "swift and round and burning", thus to some extent departing from the conception of it usually held in his time:

> "And right so as thise philosophres wryte
> That heven is swift and round and eek brenninge,
> Right so was fayre Cecilie the whyte."[1]—

In using the terms "swift and round" Chaucer must have been thinking of the *primum mobile* which, as we have seen, was thought to have a swift diurnal motion from east to west. His use of the epithet "burning" is in conformity with the mediaeval conception of the Empyrean, or heaven of pure light as it is described by Dante.

Chaucer does not describe the form and location of hell as definitely as does Dante, but the idea which he presents of it by incidental allusions, whether or not this was the view of it he himself held, is practically the one commonly held in his day. That hell is located somewhere within the depths of the earth is suggested in the *Knightes Tale;*[2]—

> "His felawe wente and soghte him down in helle;"

and in the *Man of Lawes Tale;*[3]

> 'O serpent under femininitee,
> Lyk to the serpent depe in helle y-bounde,"

In the *Persones Tale* hell is described as a horrible pit to which no natural light penetrates, filled with smoking flames and presided over by devils who await an opportunity to draw sinful souls to their punishment.[4] Elsewhere in the same tale the parson describes hell as a region of disorder, the only place in the world not subject to the universal laws of nature, and attributes this idea of it to Job:

---

[1]*The Seconde Nonnes Tale*, G. 113-115.
[2]A. 1200.
[3]B. 300 ff.
[4]*The Persones Tale*, I. 169 ff.: "ther shal the sterne and wrothe Iuge sitte above, and under him the horrible put of helle open to

"And eek Iob seith: that 'in helle is noon ordre
of rule.' And al-be-it so that god hath creat alle
thinges in right ordre, and no-thing with-outen
ordre, but alle thinges been ordeyned and nom-
bred; yet nathelees they that been dampned been
no-thing in ordre, ne holden noon ordre."[1]

The word purgatory seldom occurs in a literal sense
in Chaucer's poetry, but the figurative use of it is frequent.
When the Wife of Bath is relating her experiences in
married life she tells us that she was her fourth husband's
purgatory.[2] The old man, Ianuarie[3], contemplating marriage, fears that he may lose hope of heaven hereafter,
because he will have his heaven here on earth in the joys of
wedded life. His friend Iustinus sarcastically tells him
that perhaps his wife will be his purgatory, God's instrument of punishment, so that when he dies his soul will skip
to heaven quicker than an arrow from the bow. To Arcite,
released from prison on condition that he never again enter
Theseus' lands, banishment will be a worse fate than the
purgatory of life imprisonment, for then even the sight of
Emelye will be denied him:

> "He seyde, 'Allas that day that I was born!
> Now is my prison worse than biforn;
> Now is me shape eternally to dwelle
> Noght in purgatorie, but in helle.' "[4]

The idea of purgatory, not as a place definitely
located like Dante's Mount of Purgatory, but rather as a
period of punishment and probation, is expressed in these
lines from *The Parlement of Foules* (78-84):

---

destroyen him that moot biknowen hise sinnes, whiche sinnes openly
been shewed biforn god and biforn every creature. And on the left
syde, mo develes than herte may bithinke, for to harie and drawe the
sinful soules to the pyne of helle. And with-inne the hertes of folk
shal be the bytinge conscience, and withoute-forth shal be the world
al brenninge,"
[1]*The Persones Tale*, I. 216-217.
[2]*The Wife of Bath's Prologue*, D. 489.
[3]*The Marchantes Tale*, E. 1645 ff.
[4]*The Knightes Tale*, A. 1224-7.

> "'But brekers of the lawe, soth to seyne,
> And lecherous folk, after that they be dede,
> Shul alwey whirle aboute therthe in peyne,
> Til many a world be passed, out of drede,
> And than, for-yeven alle hir wikked dede,
> Than shul they come unto that blisful place,
> To which to comen god thee sende his grace!' "

Chaucer uses the idea of paradise for poetical purposes quite as often as that of purgatory. He expresses the highest degree of earthly beauty or joy by comparing it with paradise. Criseyde's face is said to be like the image of paradise.[1] Again, in extolling the married life, the poet says that its virtues are such

> " 'That in this world it is a paradys.' "[2]

And later in the same tale, woman is spoken of as
> "mannes help and his confort,
> His paradys terrestre and his disport."[3]

When Aeneas reaches Carthage he
> "is come to Paradys
> Out of the swolow of helle, and thus in Ioye
> Remembreth him of his estat in Troye."[4]

Chaucer mentions paradise several times in its literal sense as the abode of Adam and Eve before their fall. In the *Monkes Tale* we are told that Adam held sway over all paradise excepting one tree.[5] Again, the pardoner speaks of the expulsion of Adam and Eve from paradise:

> "Adam our fader, and his wyf also,
> Fro Paradys to labour and to wo
> Were driven for that vyce, it is no drede;
> For whyl that Adam fasted, as I rede,

---

[1]*Troilus and Criseyde*, Bk. IV. 864.
[2]*Marchantes Tale*, E. 1265.
[3]*Ibid.* E. 1331-1332.
[4]*The Legend of Good Women*, III. 1103 ff.
[5]*The Monkes Tale*, B. 3200.

He was in Paradys; and whan that he
Eet of the fruyt defended on the tree,
Anon he was out-cast to wo and peyne."[1]

5. *The Four Elements.*

The idea of four elements[2] has its origin in the attempts of the early Greek cosmologists to discover the ultimate principle of reality in the universe

Thales reached the conclusion that this principle was water, Anaximines, that it was air, and Heraclcitus, fire, while Parmenides supposed two elements, fire or light, subtle and rarefied, and earth or night, dense and heavy. Empedocles of Agrigentum (about 450 B. C.) assumed as primary elements all four—fire, air, water, and earth—of which each of his predecessors had assumed only one or two. To explain the manifold phenomena of nature he supposed them to be produced by combinations of the elements in different proportions through the attractive and repulsive forces of 'love' and 'discord.' This arbitrary assumption of four elements, first made by Empedocles, persisted in the popular imagination throughout the Middle Ages and is, like other cosmological ideas of antiquity, sometimes reflected in the poetry of the time.

The elements in mediaeval cosmology were assigned to a definite region of the universe. Being mortal and imperfect they occupied four spheres below the moon, the elemental region or region of imperfection, as distinguished from the ethereal region above the moon. Immediately within the sphere of the moon came that of Fire, below this the Air, then Water, and lowest of all the solid sphere of Earth.

---

[1]*The Pardoneres Tale*, C. 505-511.

[2]In the time of Hamurabi, 2,000 years before Christ, the Chaldeans worshipped as beneficent or formidable powers, the Earth, that may give or refuse sustenance to man, the Waters that fertilize or devastate, the Winds that blow from the four quarters of the world, Fire that warms or devours and all forces of nature which, in their sidereal religion, they confounded with the stars, giving them the generic name of 'Elements.' But the system that recognizes only four elements as the original sources of all that exists in nature, was created by the Greek philosophers.

See F. Cumont, *Astrology and Religion among the Greeks and Romans* (1912), p. 33.

Fire being the most ethereal of the elements constantly tends to rise upward, while Earth sinks towards the center of the universe. This contrast is a favorite idea with Dante, who says in the *Paradiso* i. 112-117:

> " 'wherefore they move to diverse ports o'er the
>   great sea of being, and each one with
>   instinct given it to bear it on.
> This beareth the fire toward the moon; this
>   is the mover in the hearts of things that die;
>   this doth draw the earth together and unite it.' "

Elsewhere Dante describes the lightning as fleeing its proper place when it strikes the earth:

> " 'but lightning, fleeing its proper site, ne'er
>   darted as dost thou who art returning thither.' "[1]

And again:

> " 'so from this course sometimes departeth the
>   creature that hath power, thus thrust, to swerve
>   to-ward some other part,
> (even as fire may be seen to dart down from
>   the cloud) if its first rush be wrenched aside
>   to earth by false seeming pleasure.' "[2]

The same thought of the tendency of fire to rise and of earth to sink is found in Chaucer's translation of Boethius:[3]

> "Thou bindest the elements by noumbres pro-
> porcionables, ... that the fyr, that is purest,
> ne flee nat over hye, ne that the hevinesse ne drawe
> nat adoun over-lowe the erthes that ben plounged
> in the wateres."

Chaucer does not make specific mention of the spheres of the elements, but he tells us plainly that each element has been assigned its proper region from which it may not escape:

[1] *Paradiso* i. 92-93.
[2] *Paradiso* i. 130-135.
[3] Book III.: Metre IX. 13 ff.

> "For with that faire cheyne of love he bond
> The fyr, the eyr, the water, and the lond
> In certeyn boundes, that they may nat flee;"[1]

The position of the elements in the universe is nevertheless made clear without specific reference to their respective spheres. The spirit of the slain Troilus ascends through the spheres to the seventh heaven, leaving behind the elements:

> "And whan that he was slayn in this manere,
> His lighte goost ful blisfully is went
> Up to the holownesse of the seventh spere,
> In converse letinge every element."[2]

"Every element" here obviously means the sphere of each element; "holownesse" means concavity and "in convers" means 'on the reverse side.' The meaning of the passage is, then, that Troilus' spirit ascends to the concave side of the seventh sphere from which he can look down upon the spheres of the elements, which have their convex surfaces towards him. This passage is of particular interest for the further reason that it shows that even in Chaucer's century people still thought of the spheres as having material existence.

The place and order of the elements is more definitely suggested in a passage from *Boethius* in which philosophical contemplation is figuratively described as an ascent of thought upward through the spheres:

> " 'I have, forsothe, swifte fetheres that surmounten the heighte of hevene. When the swifte thought hath clothed it-self in the fetheres, it despyseth the hateful erthes, and surmounteth the roundnesse of the grete ayr; and it seeth the cloudes behinde his bak; and passeth the heighte of the region of the fyr, that eschaufeth by the swifte moevinge of the firmament, til that he areyseth him in-to the houses that beren the sterres, and ioyneth his weyes with the sonne Phebus, and felawshipeth the wey of the olde colde Saturnus.' "[3]

---

[1]*The Knightes Tale*, A. 2991-3.
[2]*Troilus and Criseyde*, V. 1807-10.
[3]*Boethius*, Book IV; Metre I. 1 ff.

In this passage all the elemental regions except that of water are alluded to and in the order which, in the Middle Ages, they were supposed to follow. When in the *Hous of Fame*, Chaucer is borne aloft into the heavens by Jupiter's eagle, he is reminded of this passage in Boethius and alludes to it:

> "And tho thoughte I upon Boece,
> That writ, 'a thought may flee so hye,
> With fetheres of Philosophye,
> To passen everich element;
> And whan he hath so fer y-went,
> Than may be seen, behind his bak,
> Cloud, and al that I of spak.' "[1]

Empedocles, as we have seen, taught that the variety in the universe was caused by the binding together of the four elements in different proportions through the harmonizing principle of love, or by their separation through hate, the principle of discord. We find this idea also reflected in Chaucer who obviously got it from Boethius. Love is the organizing principle of the universe; if the force of love should in any wise abate, all things would strive against each other and the universe be transformed into chaos.[2]

The elements were thought to be distinguished from one another by peculiar natures or attributes. Thus the nature of fire was *hot* and *dry*, that of water *cold* and *moist*,

---

[1]*The Hous of Fame*, II. 972-978.
[2]*Boethius*, Book II.: Metre VIII. 1. 1 ff.
"That the world with stable feith varieth acordable chaunginges; that the contrarious qualitee of elements holden among hemself aliaunce perdurable;. . . . . . —al this acordaunce of things is bounden with Love, that governeth erthe and see, and hath also commaundements to the hevenes. And yif this Love slakede the brydeles, alle things that now loven hem to-gederes wolden maken a bataile continuely, and stryven to fordoon the fasoun of this worlde, the whiche they now leden in acordable feith by faire moevinges."
The thought of love as the harmonizing bond between diverse elements is dealt with more poetically in *Troilus and Criseyde*, Bk. III. 1744-1757.
" 'Love, that of erthe and see hath governaunce,
Love, that his hestes hath in hevene hye,
. . . .
That that the world with feyth, which that is stable,
Dyverseth so his stoundes concordinge,

that of air *cold* and *dry,* and that of earth *hot* and *moist.*[1]
Chaucer alludes to these distinguishing attributes of the
elements a number of times, as, for example, in *Boethius,*
III,: Metre 9. 14 ff.:

> "Thou bindest the elements by noumbres
> proporciounables, that the colde thinges mowen
> acorden with the hote thinges, and the drye thinges
> with the moiste thinges";

In conclusion it should be said that all creatures oc-
cupying the elemental region or realm of imperfection
below the moon were thought to have been created not directly by God but by Nature as his "vicaire" or deputy, or, in
other words, by an inferior agency. Chaucer alludes to
this in *The Parlement of Foules* briefly thus:

> "Nature, the vicaire of thalmyghty lorde,
> That hoot, cold, hevy, light, (and) moist and dreye
> Hath knit by even noumbre of acorde,"[2]

and more at length in *The Phisiciens Tale.* Chaucer says
of the daughter of Virginius that nature had formed her
of such excellence that she might have said of her creation:

> " 'lo!   I, Nature,
> Thus can I forme and peynte a creature,
> Whan that me list; who can me countrefete?
> Pigmalion noght, though he ay forge and bete,
> Or grave, or peynte; for I dar wel seyn,
> Apelles, Zanzis, sholde werche in veyn,
> Outher to grave or peynte or forge or bete,
> If they presumed me to countrefete.
> For he that is the former principal
> Hath maked me his vicaire general,
> To forme and peynten erthely creaturis
> Right as me list, and ech thing in my cure is
> Under the mone, that may wane and waxe,

That elements that been so discordable
Holden a bond perpetuely duringe,
That Phebus mote his rosy day forth bringe,
And that the mone hath lordship over the nightes,
Al this doth Love; ay heried be his mightes!' "
[1]Skeat, *Notes to Boethius,* II.: Metre 9, 1. 14.
[2]11.379-381.

> And for my werk right no-thing wol I axe;
> My lord and I ben ful of oon accord;
> I made hir to the worship of my lord.' "[1]

What is of especial interest for our purposes is found in the five lines of this passage beginning "For he that is the former principal," etc. "Former principal" means 'creator principal' or the chief creator. God is the chief creator; therefore there must be other or inferior creators. Nature is a creator of inferior rank whom God has made his "vicaire" or deputy and whose work it is to create and preside over all things beneath the sphere of the moon.

IV

CHAUCER'S ASTRONOMY

Chaucer's treatment of astronomical lore in his poetry differs much from his use of it in his prose writings. In poetical allusions to heavenly phenomena, much attention to detail and a pedantic regard for accuracy would be inappropriate. References to astronomy in Chaucer's poetry are, as a rule rather brief, specific but not technical, often purely conventional but always truly poetic. There are, indeed, occasional passages in Chaucer's poetry showing so detailed a knowledge of observational[2] astronomy that they would seem astonishing and, to many people, out of place, in modern poetry. They were not so in Chaucer's time, when the exigencies of practical life demanded of the ordinary man a knowledge of astronomy far surpassing that possessed by most of our contemporaries. Harry Bailly in the *Introduction to the Man of Lawes Tale* determines the day of the month and hour of the day by making calculations from the observed position of the sun in the sky, and from the length of shadows, although, says Chaucer, "he were not depe expert in lore."[3] Such re-

---

[1]*The Phisiciens Tale*, C. 11-26.
[2]See Appendix, I.
[3]B. 1 ff.

ferences to technical details of astronomy as we find in this passage are, however, not common in Chaucer's poetry; in his *Treatise on the Astrolabe,* on the other hand, a professedly scientific work designed to instruct his young son Louis in those elements of astronomy and astrology that were necessary for learning the use of the astrolabe, we have sufficient evidence that he was thoroughly familiar with the technical details of the astronomical science of his day.

In Chaucer's poetry the astronomical references employed are almost wholly of two kinds: references showing the time of day or season of the year at which the events narrated are supposed to take place; and figurative allusions for purposes of illustration or comparison. Figurative uses of astronomy in Chaucer vary from simple similes as in the *Prologue to the Canterbury Tales,* where the friar's eyes are compared to twinkling stars[1] to extended allegories like the *Compleynt of Mars* in which the myth of Venus and Mars is related by describing the motions of the planets Venus and Mars for a certain period during which Venus overtakes Mars, they are in conjunction[2] for a short time, and then Venus because of her greater apparent velocity leaves Mars behind. One of the most magnificent astronomical figures employed by Chaucer is in the *Hous of*

> "Our Hoste sey wel that the brighte sonne
> The ark of his artificial day had ronne
> The fourthe part, and half an houre, and more;
> And though he were not depe expert in lore,
> He wiste it was the eightetethe day
> Of April, that is messager to May;
> And sey wel that the shadwe of every tree
> Was as in lengthe the same quantitee
> That was the body erect that caused it.
> And therefor by the shadwe he took his wit
> That Phebus, which that shoon so clere and brighte,
> Degrees was fyve and fourty clombe on highte;
> And for that day, as in that latitude,
> It was ten of the clokke, he gan conclude,
> And sodeynly he plighte his hors aboute."

For Chaucer's accuracy in this reference see Appendix II.

[1]*Prologue,* 267-68.

[2]Planets are said to be in conjunction with one another when they appear as one object or very close together within a limited area of the sky.

Fame. Chaucer looks up into the heavens and sees a great golden eagle near the sun, a sight so splendid that men could never have beheld its equal 'unless the heaven had won another sun:'

"Hit was of golde, and shone so bright,
That never saw men such a sighte,
But-if the heven hadde y-wonne
Al newe of golde another sonne;
So shoon the egles fethres brighte,
And somwhat dounward gan hit lighte."[1]

Besides mentioning the heavenly bodies in time references and figurative allusions, Chaucer also employs them often in descriptions of day and night, of dawn and twilight, and of the seasons. It is with a poet's joy in the warm spring sun that he writes:

"Bright was the day, and blew the firmament,
Phebus of gold his stremes doun hath sent,
To gladen every flour with his warmnesse."[2]

and with a poet's delight in the new life and vigor that nature puts forth when spring comes that he writes the lines:

"Forgeten had the erthe his pore estat
Of winter, that him naked made and mat,
And with his swerd of cold so sore greved;
Now hath the atempre sonne al that releved
That naked was, and clad hit new agayn."[3]

Chaucer's astronomical allusions, then, except in the *Treatise on the Astrolabe* and in his translation of *Boethius de Consolatione Philosophiae,* in which a philosophical interest in celestial phenomena is displayed, are almost in-

---

[1]*The Hous of Fame,* Book I. 503-8. Cf. Dante, *Paradiso* i. 58-63:
"I not long endured him, nor yet so little but that I saw him
  sparkle all around, like iron issuing molten from the furnace.
And, of a sudden, meseemed that day was added unto day, as
[2]*The Marchantes Tale,* E. 2219-21.
[3]*Prologue to the Legend of Good Women,* 125-9.
  though he who hath the power, had adorned heaven with a
  second sun."

variably employed with poetic purpose. These poetical allusions to heavenly phenomena, however, together with the more technical and detailed references in Chaucer's prose works give evidence of a rather extensive knowledge of astronomy. With all of the important observed movements of the heavenly bodies he was perfectly familiar and it is rather remarkable how many of these he uses in his poetry without giving one the feeling that he is airing his knowledge.

1. *The Sun*

Of all the heavenly bodies the one most often mentioned and employed for poetic purposes by Chaucer is the sun. Chaucer has many epithets for the sun, but speaks of him perhaps most often in the classical manner as Phebus or Apollo. He is called the "golden tressed Phebus"[1] or the "laurer-crowned Phebus;"[2] and when he makes Mars flee from Venus' palace he is called the "candel of Ielosye."[3] In the following passage Chaucer uses three different epithets for the sun within two lines:

> "The dayes honour, and the hevenes ye,
> The nightes fo, al this clepe I the sonne,
> Gan westren faste, and dounward for to wrye,
> As he that hadde his dayes cours y-ronne;"[4]

Sometimes Chaucer gives the sun the various accessories with which classical myth had endowed him—the four swift steeds, the rosy chariot and fiery torches:

> "And Phebus with his rosy carte sone
> Gan after that to dresse him up to fare."[5]
> ' "now am I war
> That Pirous and tho swifte stedes three,
> Which that drawen forth the sonnes char,

---

[1] *Troilus and Criseyde*, V. 8.
[2] *Ibid.* V, 1107.
[3] *Compleynt of Mars*, 7.
The epithet "candel of Ielosye" is an allusion to the classical myth according to which Phoebus (the Sun), having discovered the amour between Mars and Venus, revealed it to Vulcan thus arousing him to jealousy.
[4] *Troilus and Criseyde*, II, 904-907.
[5] *Ibid.* V. 278-279.

Hath goon some by-path in despyt of me;' "[1]

"Phebus, that was comen hastely
Within the paleys-yates sturdely,
With torche in honde, of which the stremes brighte
On Venus chambre knokkeden ful lighte."[2]

Almost always when Chaucer wishes to mention the time of day at which the events he is relating take place, he does so by describing the sun's position in the sky or the direction of his motion. We can imagine that Chaucer often smiled as he did this, for he sometimes humorously apologizes for his poetical conceits and conventions by expressing his idea immediately afterwards in perfectly plain terms. Such is the case in the passage already quoted where Chaucer refers to the sun by the epithets "dayes honour," "hevenes ye," and "nightes fo" and then explains them by saying "al this clepe I the sonne;" and in the lines:

"Til that the brighte sonne loste his hewe;
For thorisonte hath reft the sonne his light;"

explained by the simple words:

"This is as muche to seye as it was night."[3]

Thus it is that Chaucer's poetic references to the apparent daily motion of the sun about the earth are nearly always simply in the form of allusions to his rising and setting. Canacee in the *Squieres Tale*, (F. 384 ff.) is said to rise at dawn, looking as bright and fresh as the spring sun risen four degrees from the horizon.

"Up ryseth fresshe Canacee hir-selve,
As rody and bright as dooth the yonge sonne,
That in the Ram[4] is four degrees up-ronne;
Noon hyer was he, whan she redy was;"

Many of these references to the rising and setting of the sun might be mentioned, if space permitted, simply for their beauty as poetry. One of the most beautiful is the following:

---

[1]*Troilus and Criseyde*, III. 1702-5.
[2]*Compleynt of Mars*, 81-84.
[3]*Frankeleyns Tale*, F. 1016-18.
[4]See Appendix III.

"And fyry Phebus ryseth up so brighte,
That al the orient laugheth of the lighte,
And with his stremes dryeth in the greves
The silver dropes, hanging on the leves."[1]

When, in the *Canterbury Tales*, the manciple has finished his tale, Chaucer determines the time by observing the position of the sun and by making calculations from the length of his own shadow:

"By that the maunciple hadde his tale al ended,
The sonne fro the south lyne was descended
So lowe, that he nas nat, to my sighte,
Degrees nyne and twenty as in highte.
Foure of the clokke it was tho, as I gesse;
For eleven foot, or litel more or lesse,
My shadwe was at thilke tyme, as there,
Of swich feet as my lengthe parted were
In six feet equal of porporcioun."[2]

We must not omit mention of the humorous touch with which Chaucer, in the mock heroic tale of *Chanticleer and the Fox* told by the nun's priest, makes even the rooster determine the time of day by observing the altitude of the sun in the sky:

"Chauntecleer, in al his pryde,
His seven wyves walkyng by his syde,
Caste up his eyen to the brighte sonne,
That in the signe of Taurus hadde y-ronne
Twenty degrees and oon, and somewhat more;
And knew by kynde, and by noon other lore,
That it was pryme, and crew with blisful stevene.
'The sonne,' he sayde, 'is clomben up on hevene
Fourty degrees and oon, and more, y-wis.' "[3]

---

[1]*Knightes Tale*, A 1493-1496.
[2]*Parson's Prologue*, I. 1-9. See Appendix IV.
[3]*Nonne Preestes Tale*, B. 4381-89. Chaucer has already indicated the date as May 3 by saying that March is complete and thirty-two days have passed besides. (l. 4379). That the sun would on May 3 have passed the 21st degree of Aries can be verified by reference to Fig. 1 in Skeat's *Introduction to the Astrolabe*. A straight edge ing May 3 would cross the circle of the zodiacal signs at a point a little past the 21st degree of Aries.

Moreover, this remarkable rooster observed that the sun
had passed the twenty-first degree in Taurus, and we are
told elsewhere that he knew each ascension of the equil-
noctial and crew at each; that is, he crew every hour, as 15°
of the equinoctial correspond to an hour:

"Wel sikerer was his crowing in his logge,
Than is a clokke, or an abbey orlogge.
By nature knew he ech ascencioun[1]
Of th' equinoxial in thilke toun;
For whan degrees fiftene were ascended,
Thanne crew he, that it mighte nat ben amended."[2]

Chaucer announces the approach of evening by describing the position and appearance of the sun more often
than any other time of the day. In the *Legend of Good
Women* he speaks of the sun's leaving the south point[3]
of his daily course and approaching the west:

"Whan that the sonne out of the south gan weste,"[4]

and again of his westward motion in the lines:

"And whan that hit is eve, I rene blyve,
As sone as ever the sonne ginneth weste,"[5]

Elsewhere Chaucer refers to the setting of the sun by saying that he has completed his "ark divine" and may no
longer remain on the horizon,[6] or by saying that the 'horizon has bereft the sun of his light.'[7]

Chaucer's references to the daily motion of the sun
about the earth are apt to sound to us like purely poetical
figures, so accustomed are we to refer to the sun, what we
know to be the earth's rotatory motion, by speaking of his
apparent daily motion thus figuratively as if it were real.
Chaucer's manner of describing the revolution of the heavenly bodies about the earth and his application of poetic
epithets to them *are* figurative, but the motion itself was

[1]Ascension means 'ascending degree.'
[2]*Nonne Preestes Tale*, B. 4043-4048.
[3]The sun reaches his farthest point to the south at noon when
on the meridian. See appendix I.
[4]*Prologue*, 197.
[5]*Ibid.* 60-61.
[6]*Marchantes Tale*, E. 1795-7.
[7]*Frankeleyns Tale*, F. 1016-17.

meant literally and was believed in by the men of his century, because only the geocentric system of astronomy was then known.   If Chaucer had been in advance of his century in this respect there would certainly be some hint of the fact in his writings.

References in Chaucer to the sun's yearly motion are in the same sense literal.   The apparent motion of the sun along the ecliptic,[1] which we know to be caused by the earth's yearly motion in an elliptical orbit around the sun, was then believed to be an actual movement of the sun carried along by his revolving sphere.   Like the references to the sun's daily movements those that mention his yearly motion along the ecliptic are also usually time references. The season of the year is indicated by defining the sun's position among the signs of the zodiac.   The Canterbury pilgrims set out on their journey in April when

> "the yonge sonne
> Hath in the Ram his halfe course y-ronne."[2]

In describing the month of May, Chaucer does not fail to mention the sun's position in the zodiac:

> "In May, that moder is of monthes glade,
> That fresshe floures, blewe, and whyte, and rede,
> Ben quike agayn, that winter dede made,
> And ful of bawme is fletinge every mede;
> Whan Phebus doth his brighte bemes sprede
> Right in the whyte Bole, it so bitidde
> As I shal singe, on Mayes day the thridde,"[3] etc.

The effect of the sun's declination in causing change of seasons[4] is mentioned a number of times in Chaucer's

---

See Appendix I. 82 ff., 84 ff.

[2]*Prologue to the Canterbury Tales*, A. 7-8.

At the beginning of April the sun is a little past the middle of Aries and at the beginning of May, roughly speaking, he is in the middle of Taurus.   Thus the sun in April runs a half-course in Aries and a half-course in Taurus.   Chaucer means here that the former of these half-courses is completed, so that it is some time after the eleventh of April.

[3]*Troilus and Criseyde*, II. 50-56.   On the third of May, in Chaucer's time, the sun would be past the twentieth degree of Taurus.

[4]The sun's declination means his angular distance north or south of the celestial equator.   The solstices mark his maximum declination north or south.   See Appendix I. 83 ff.

poetry. The poet makes a general reference to the fact in a passage of exquisite beauty from *Troilus and Criseyde* where he says that the sun has thrice returned to his lofty position in the sky and melted away the snows of winter:

> "The golden-trèssed Phebus heighe on-lofte
> Thryes hadde alle with his bemes shene
> The snowes molte, and Zephirus as ofte
> Y-brought ayein the tendre leves grene,
> Sin that the sone of Ecuba the quene
> Bigan to love hir first, for whom his sorwe
> Was al, that she departe sholde a-morwe."[1]

More interesting astronomically but of less interest as poetry is his reference to the sun's declination and its effect on the seasons in the *Frankeleyns Tale*, because here Chaucer uses the word 'declination' and states that it is the cause of the seasons. The reference is the beginning of Aurelius' prayer to Apollo, or the sun:

> " 'Apollo, God and governour
> Of every plaunte, herbe, tree and flour,
> That yevest, after thy declinacioun,
> To ech of hem his tyme and his sesoun,
> As thyn herberwe chaungeth lowe or hye;' "[2]

Once again in the *Frankeleyns Tale* Chaucer refers to the sun's declination and the passage of the seasons:

> "Phebus wex old, and hewed lyk latoun,[3]
> That in his hote declinacioun
> Shoon as the burned gold with stremes brighte;
> But now in Capricorn adoun he lighte,
> Wher-as he shoon ful pale, I dar wel seyn."[4]

Chaucer is here contrasting the sun's appearance in summer and winter. In his hot declination (his greatest northward declination in Cancer, about June 21) he shines as burnished gold, but when he reaches Capricornus, his greatest southward declination (about December 21) he appears

---

[1]V. 8-14.
[2]*Frankeleyns Tale*, F. 1031-35. See Appendix V.
[3]Latoun was a compound metal containing chiefly copper and zinc.
[4]F. 1245-49.

'old' and has a dull coppery color, no longer that of brilliant gold.

2. *The Moon*

From those references to the moon that occur in Chaucer's poetry alone, it would be impossible to determine just how much he knew of the peculiarities of her apparent movements; for he alludes to the moon's motion and positions much less frequently and with much less detail than to those of the sun. But a passage in the prologue to the *Astrolabe* leaves it without doubt that Chaucer was quite familiar with lunar phenomena. In stating what the treatise is to contain, he says of the fourth part: "The whiche ferthe partie in special shal shewen a table of the verray moeving of the mone from houre to houre, every day and in every signe, after thyn almenak; upon which table ther folwith a canon, suffisant to teche as wel the maner of the wyrking of that same conclusioun, as to knowe in oure orizonte with which degree of the zodiac that the mone ariseth in any latitude;"[1] As a matter of fact the treatise as first contemplated by Chaucer was never finished; only the first two parts were written. But Chaucer would scarcely have written thus definitely of his plan for the fourth part of the work unless he had had fairly complete knowledge of the phenomena connected with the moon's movements.

The moon, in Chaucer's imagination, must have occupied rather an insignificant position among the heavenly bodies as far as appealing to his sense of beauty was concerned, for we find in his poetry no descriptions of her appearance that can compare with his descriptions of the sun or even of the stars. He speaks of moonrise in the the most general way:

> "hit fil, upon a night,
> When that the mone up-reysed had her light,
> This noble quene un-to her reste wente;"[2]

---

[1]*Astrolabe, Prologue*, 64-70.
[2]*Legend of Good Women*, III. 1162-4.

He applies to her only a few epithets, the most eulogistic
of which is "Lucina the shene."[1] In comparing the sun
with the other heavenly bodies the poet mentions the moon
among the rest without distinction, as inferior to the sun:

> "For I dar swere, withoute doute,
> That as the someres sonne bright
> Is fairer, clerer, and hath more light
> Than any planete, (is) in heven,
> The mone, or the sterres seven,
> For al the worlde, so had she
> Surmounted hem alle of beaute," etc.[2]

On the other hand, the stars are elsewhere said to be like
small candles in comparison with the moon:

> "And cleer as (is) the mone-light,
> Ageyn whom alle the sterres semen
> But smale candels, as we demen."[3]

Whenever Chaucer mentions the moon's position in the
heavens he does so by reference to the signs of the zodiac[4]
and, as in the case of the sun, usually with the purpose of
showing time. In the *Marchantes Tale* he expresses the
passage of four days thus:

> "The mone that, at noon, was, thilke day
> That Ianuarie hath wedded fresshe May,
> In two of Taur, was in-to Cancre gliden;
> So long hath Maius in hir chambre biden,"[5]

and a few lines further on he states the fact explicitly:

---

[1]*Troilus and Criseyde*, IV. 1591.
[2]*Book of the Duchesse*, 820-26.
[3]*Romaunt of the Rose*, 1010-12.
[4]See Appendix VI.
[5]*Marchantes Tale*, E. 1885-8.
To pass from the second degree of Taurus into Cancer the moon
would have to traverse the remaining twenty-eight degrees of
Taurus, thirty of Gemini and at least one of Cancer, making 59° of
the zodiac in all. For the moon to do this is possible, as Skeat has
shown. See Appendix VII.

"The fourthe day compleet fro noon to noon,
Whan that the heighe masse was y-doon,
In halle sit this Ianuarie, and May
As fresh as is the brighte someres day."[1]

When Criseyde leaves Troilus to go to the Greek army
she promises to return to Troy within the time that it will
take the moon to pass from Aries through Leo, that is, within ten days:

" 'And trusteth this, that certes, herte swete,
Er Phebus suster, Lucina the shene,
The Leoun passe out of this Ariete,
I wol ben here, with-outen any wene.
I mene, as helpe me Iuno, hevenes quene,
The tenthe day, but-if that deeth me assayle,
I wol yow seen, with-outen any fayle.' "[2]

But while the moon is quickly traversing the part of her
course from Aries to Leo, Criseyde, pressed by Diomede,
is changing her mind about returning to Troy, and by the
appointed tenth day has decided to remain with the Greeks:

"And Cynthea[3] hir char-hors over-raughte
To whirle out of the Lyon, if she mighte;
And Signifer[4] his candeles shewed brighte,
Whan that Criseyde un-to hir bedde wente
In-with hir fadres faire brighte tente.

. . . . , . . .
. . . . . . and thus bigan to brede
The cause why, the sothe for to telle,
That she tok fully purpos for to dwelle."[5]

The passage of time is also indicated in Chaucer's
poetry by reference to the recurrence of the moon's phases.
In the *Legend of Good Women*, Phillis writes to the false

---

[1]*Marchantes Tale*, E. 1893-6.
[2]*Troilus and Criseyde.* IV. 1590-96. Chaucer's reference to the
moon's motion is again correct. It would, in fact, take the moon about
ten days to pass from Aries through Leo, traversing four signs,
Taurus, Gemini, Cancer, and Leo, or about one-third of the whole
zodiac. See Skeat, *Notes to Troilus and Criseyde*, p. 494.
[3]The moon.
[4]The 'sign-bearer'; that is, the zodiac. His candles are of course
the stars and planets that appear in the zodiac.
[5]*Troilus and Criseyde,* V. 1018-22; 1027-29.

Demophon saying that the moon has passed through its phases four times since he went away and thrice since the time he promised to return:

> " 'Your anker, which ye in our haven leyde,
> Highte us, that ye wolde comen, out of doute,
> Or that the mone ones wente aboute.
> But tymes foure the mone hath hid her face
> Sin thilke day ye wente fro this place,
> And foure tymes light the world again.' "[1]

Chaucer refers more often to the phases of the moon than to any other lunar phenomenon, but most of these references to her phases are used for the sake of comparison or illustration and give us little idea of the extent of Chaucer's knowledge. Mars in his 'compleynt' says that the lover

> "Hath ofter wo then changed is the mone."[2]

The rumors in the house of fame are given times of waxing and waning like the moon:

> "Thus out at holes gonne wringe
> Every tyding streight to Fame;
> And she gan yeven eche his name,
> After hir disposicioun,
> And yaf hem eek duracioun,
> Some to wexe and wane sone,
> As dooth the faire whyte mone,
> And leet hem gon."[3]

Chaucer briefly describes the crescent moon by calling her

> "The bente mone with hir hornes pale"[4]

In Troilus' prayer to the moon, the line

> " 'I saugh thyn hornes olde eek by the morwe,' "[5]

is practically the only one in which Chaucer gives any hint of the times at which the moon in her various phases may be seen. The phase of the 'new moon,' when the moon is in

---

[1]*Legend of Good Women*, 2501-6.
[2]*Compleynt of Mars*, 235.
[3]*Hous of Fame*, 2110-17.
[4]*Troilus and Criseyde*, III. 624.
[5]*Ibid.* V. 652. "by the morwe" means 'early in the morning.'

conjunction with the sun (i. e., between the earth and the sun, so that we cannot see the illuminated hemisphere of the moon) is mentioned in the same poem:

> "Right sone upon the chaunging of the mone,
> Whan lightles is the world a night or tweyne."[1]

There is a very definite description of three of the moon's phases in the following passage from *Boethius*:[2] "so that the mone som-tyme shyning with hir ful hornes, meting with alle the bemes of the sonne hir brother, hydeth the sterres that ben lesse; and som-tyme, whan the mone, pale with hir derke hornes, approcheth the sonne, leseth hir lightes;" The moon 'shining with her full horns' means with her horns filled up as at full moon when she is in a position opposite both earth and sun so that she reflects upon the earth all the rays of the sun. The moon "with derke hornes" refers of course to the waning moon, a thin crescent near the sun and almost obscured in his light, which approaching nearer the sun is entirely lost to our view in his rays and becomes the new moon.

Chaucer's most interesting references to the moon are found in the prayer of Aurelius to the sun in the *Frankeleyns Tale*. Dorigen has jestingly promised to have pity on Aurelius as soon as he shall remove all the rocks from along the coast of Brittany, and Aurelius prays to the sun, or Apollo, to help him by enlisting the aid of the moon, in accomplishing this feat. The sun's sister, Lucina, or the moon, is chief goddess of the sea; just as she desires to follow the sun and be quickened and illuminated by him, so the sea desires to follow her:

> " 'Your blisful suster, Lucina the shene,
> That of the see is chief goddesse and quene,
> Though Neptunus have deitee in the see,
> Yet emperesse aboven him is she:
> Ye knowen wel, lord, that right as hir desyr
> Is to be quiked and lightned of your fyr,

[1]*Troilus and Criseyde, III.* EDT-EJ. See Appendix VIII. p. 91.
[2]Book I.: Metre V. 4-7.

For which she folweth yow ful bisily,
Right so the see desyreth naturelly
To folwen hir, as she that is goddesse
Bothe in the see and riveres more and lesse.' "[1]

In calling Lucina chief goddess of the sea and speaking of
the sea's desire to follow her, Chaucer is, of course allud-
ing to the moon's effect upon the tides; and in the line:

" 'Is to be quiked and lightned of your fyr,' "

the reference is to the fact that the moon derives her light
from the sun.

Instead of leaving it to the sun-god to find a way of
removing the rocks for him, Aurelius proceeds to give ex-
plicit instructions as to how this may be accomplished. As
the highest tides occur when the moon is in opposition or in
conjunction with the sun, if the moon could only be kept in
either of these positions with regard to the sun for a long
enough time, so great a flood would be produced, Aurelius
thinks, that the rocks would be washed away. So he
prays Phebus to induce the moon to slacken her speed at her
next opposition in Leo and for two years to traverse her
sphere with the same (apparent) velocity as that of the sun,
thus remaining in opposition with him:

" 'Wherfore, lord Phebus, this is my requeste—
Do this miracle, or do myn herte breste—
That now, next at this opposicioun,
Which in the signe shal be of the Leoun,
As preyeth hir so greet a flood to bringe,
That fyve fadme at the leeste it overspringe
The hyeste rokke in Armorik Briteyne;
And lat this flood endure yeres tweyne;

. . . .

Preye hir she go no faster cours than ye,
I seye, preyeth your suster that she go
No faster cours than ye thise yeres two.
Than shal she been evene atte fulle alway,

<hr>

[1]*Frankeleyns Tale*, F. 1045-54.

And spring-flood laste bothe night and day.' "[1]

References to eclipses of the moon occur seldom in Chaucer. In the second part of the *Romaunt of the Rose*, which is included in complete editions of Chaucer's works but which he almost certainly did not write, there is a description of a lunar eclipse and of its causes. Fickleness in love is compared to an eclipse:

"For it shal chaungen wonder sone,
And take eclips right as the mone,
Whan she is from us (y)-let
Thurgh erthe, that bitwixe is set
The sonne and hir, as it may falle,
Be it in party, or in alle;
The shadowe maketh her bemis merke,
And hir hornes to shewe derke,
That part where she hath lost hir lyght
Of Phebus fully, and the sight;
Til, whan the shadowe is overpast,
She is enlumined ageyn as faste,
Thurgh brightnesse of the sonne bemes
That yeveth to hir ageyn hir lemes."[2]

This passage is so clear that it needs no explanation.

An eclipse of the moon, since it is caused by the passing of the moon into the shadow of the earth, can only take place when the moon is full, that is, in *opposition* to the sun. This fact is suggested in a reference in *Boethius* to a lunar eclipse:

---

[1]*Frankeleyns Tale*, F. 1055-70. Skeat explains the lines:
          "next at this opposicioun,
     Which in the signe shal be of the Leoun,"
thus: Earlier in the poem (1. 906) May 6 is mentioned and it is on this date that the events narrated so far are supposed to have taken place. In May the sun is in Taurus, so that the moon at her next opposition would have to be in the opposite sign, Scorpio. The reference must mean therefore:—"at the next opposition that takes place with the sun in Leo," not the very next one with the sun in Taurus, nor the next with the sun in Gemini or Cancer. This reason for waiting until there should be an opposition with the sun in Leo, was astrological. Leo was the *mansion* of the Sun, so that the sun's power when in that sign would be greatest.
     [2]B. 5333-46.

"the hornes of the fulle mone wexen pale and infect by the boundes of the derke night;"[1]

In the next lines Chaucer mentions the fact that the stars which are lost to sight in the bright rays of the full moon become visible during an eclipse:

"and . . . . . the mone, derk and confuse, discovereth the sterres that she hadde y-covered by hir clere visage."[2]

3. *The Planets*

All the planets that are easily visible to the unaided eye were known in Chaucer's time and are mentioned in his writings, some of them many times. These planets are Mercury, Venus, Mars, Jupiter, and Saturn. According to the Ptolemaic system, which as we have seen, held sway in the world of learning during Chaucer's century, the sun and moon were also held to be planets, and all were supposed to revolve around the earth in concentric rings, the moon being nearest the earth, and the sun between Venus and Mars. The circular orbit of each planet was called its "deferent" and upon the deferent moved, not the planet itself, but an imaginary planet, represented by a point. The real planet moved upon a smaller circle called the "epicycle" whose center was the moving point representing the imaginary planet. The deferent of each planet was supposed to be traced as a great circle upon a transparent separate crystal sphere; and all of the crystal spheres revolved once a day around an axis passing through the poles of the heavens. As the sun and moon did not show the same irregularities[3] of motion as the planets, Ptolemy supposed these two bodies to have deferents but no epicycles. Later investigators complicated the system by adding further secondary imaginary planets, revolving in Ptolemy's epicycles and with the actual planets attached to additional corresponding epicycles. They even supposed the moon to have one, perhaps two epicycles and we shall find this notion reflected in

---

[1]Book IV.: Metre V. 8-9.
[2]Ibid.   10-11.
[3]See Appendix IX. p. ff.

Chaucer. The eighth sphere had neither deferent nor epicycle but to it were attached the fixed stars. This sphere as we have seen earlier, revolved slowly from west to east to account for the precession of the equinoxes, while a ninth sphere, the *primum mobile,* imparted to all the inner spheres their diurnal motion from east to west.

Chaucer's poetical references to the planets, as we have found to be true in the case of the sun and moon, do not give us satisfactory evidence of the extent of his knowledge, but occasional passages from his prose works again throw light on these allusions. Chaucer refers to the planets in general as 'the seven stars,' as, for instance, in the lines:

> "And with hir heed she touched hevene,
> Ther as shynen sterres sevene."[1]

and

> "To have mo floures, swiche seven
> As in the welken sterres be."[2]

Chaucer was undoubtedly familiar with the irregularities of the planetary movements, and with the theory of epicycles by which these irregular movements were in his day explained, although it is not from his poetry that we can learn the fact. He uses the word 'epicycle' only once in all his works. In the *Astrolabe* when comparing the moon's motion with that of the other planets, he says: "for sothly, the mone moeveth the contrarie from othere planetes as in hir episicle, but in non other manere."[3]

In the *Astrolabe*[4] Chaucer explains a method of determining whether a planet's motion is retrograde or direct.[5] The altitude of the planet and of any fixed star, is taken,

---

[1]*Hous of Fame,* III. 1375-6.
[2]*Book of the Duchesse,* III. 408-9.
[3]*Astrolabe,* II. 35. 17-18. The attempt to explain the moon's motion by supposing her to move in an epicycle was hopelessly wrong. Chaucer means here simply that the moon's motion in her deferent is direct like that of the other planets (their apparent motion is in the direction west to east except at short periods of retrogression) but that the moon's direction of motion in her epicycle is the reverse of that of the other planets.
[4]II. 35.
[5]See Appendix IX. p. 92 ff.

and several nights later at the time when the fixed star has the same altitude as at the previous observation, the planet's altitude is again observed.   If the planet is on the right or east side of the meridian, and its second altitude is less than its first, then the planet's motion is direct.   If the planet is on the left or west side of the meridian, and has a smaller altitude at the second observation than at the first, then the planet's motion is retrograde.   If the planet is on the east side of the meridional line when its altitude is taken and the second altitude is greater than the first, it is retrograde; and if it is on the west side and its second altitude is greater, it is direct.   This method would be correct were it not that a change in the planet's declination or angular distance from the celestial equator might render the conclusions incorrect.

Chaucer mentions the irregularity of planetary movements in *Boethius* also when he says: "and whiche sterre in hevene useth wandering recourses, y-flit by dyverse speres."[1]   The expression "y-flit by dyverse speres" may have reference only to the one motion of the planets, that is, their motion concentric to the star-sphere; or it may be used to include also their epicyclic motion. Skeat interprets the expression in the former way; but the context, it seems, would justify interpreting the words "dyverse speres" as meaning the various spheres of the planets to-gether with their epicycles; i. e., both deferents and epicycles.

Of all the planets, that most often mentioned by Chaucer is Venus, partly, no doubt, because of her greater brilliance, but probably in the main because of her greater astrological importance; for few of Chaucer's references to Venus, or to any other planet, indeed, are without astrological significance.   Chaucer refers to Venus, in the classical manner, as Hesperus when she appears as evening[2] star and as Lucifer when she is seen as the morning star: "and that the

---

[1]Book I: Metre II. 8-9.

[2]Mercury and Venus are always seen either just before sunrise or just after sunset because their distances from the sun are so comparatively small.

eve-sterre Hesperus, which that in the firste tyme of the night bringeth forth hir colde arysinges, cometh eft ayein hir used cours, and is pale *by the morwe* at the rysing of the sonne, and is thanne cleped Lucifer.[1] Her appearance as morning star is again mentioned in the same work: "and after that Lucifer the day-sterre hath chased awey the derke night, the day the fairere ledeth the rosene hors *of the sonne*,"[2] and in *Troilus and Criseyde* where it is said that

> "Lucifer, the dayes messager,
> Gan for to ryse, and out hir bemes throwe;"[3]

Elsewhere in the same poem her appearance as evening star is mentioned but she is not this time called Hesperus:

> "The brighte Venus folwede and ay taughte
> The wey, ther brode Phebus doun alighte;"[4]

Occasionally Venus is called Cytherea, from the island near which Greek myth represented her as having arisen from the sea. Thus in the *Knightes Tale*:

> "He roos, to wenden on his pilgrimage
> Un-to the blisful Citherea benigne,
> I mene Venus, honurable and digne."[5]

and in the *Parlement of Foules*;

> "Citherea! thou blisful lady swete,"[6]

The relative positions of the different planets in the heavens is suggested by allusions to the different sizes of their spheres and to their different velocities. In the *Compleynt of Mars* the comparative sizes and velocities of the spheres of Mercury, Venus and Mars are made the basis for most of the action of the poem. The greater the sphere or orbit of a planet, the slower is its apparent motion. Thus Mars in his large sphere moves about half as fast as Venus and in the poem it is planned that when Mars reaches the

---

[1]*Boethius*, Bk. I.: Metre V. 8-11.
[2]*Ibid*, Bk. III: Metre I. 6-8.
[3]*Troilus and Criseyde*, Bk. III. 1417-18.
[4]*Ibid*. V. 1016-17.
[5]A. 2214-16.
[6]113.

next palace[1] of Venus, he shall by virtue of his slower motion, wait for her to overtake him:

> "That Mars shal entre, as faste as he may glyde,
> Into hir nexte paleys, to abyde,
> Walking his cours til she had him a-take,
> And he preyde hir to haste hir for his sake."[2]

Venus in compassion for his solitude hastens to overtake her knight:

> "She hath so gret compassion of hir knight,
> That dwelleth in solitude til she come;
>
> . . . .
>
> Wherefore she spedde hir as faste in her weye,
> Almost in oon day, as he dide in tweye."[3]

When Phebus comes into the palace with his fiery torch, Mars will not flee and cannot hide, so he girds himself with sword and armour and bids Venus flee. Phebus, who in Chaucer's time was regarded as the fourth planet, can overtake Mars but not Venus because his sphere is between theirs and his motion is consequently slower than that of Venus but faster than that of Mars:

> "Flee wolde he not, ne mighte him-selven hyde.
>
> He throweth on his helm of huge wighte,
> And girt him with his swerde; and in his honde
> His mighty spere, as he was wont to fighte,
> He shaketh so that almost it to-wonde;
> Ful hevy he was to walken over londe;
> He may not holde with Venus companye,
> But bad hir fleen, lest Phebus hir espye.

---

[1]This is an astrological term. A *palace, mansion* or *house* was that zodiacal sign in which a planet was supposed to be peculiarly at home.

[2]*Compleynt of Mars*, 53-56. Mars is to hurry until he reaches Venus' palace and then advance as slowly as possible, to wait for her. Evidently Chaucer was aware of the varying apparent velocities of planetary motions.

[3]*Ibid.* 64-70. When Venus overtakes Mars they are in conjunction.

> "O woful Mars! alas! what mayst thou seyn,
> That in the paleys of thy disturbaunce
> Art left behinde, in peril to be sleyn?
>
> . . . .
>
> That thou nere swift, wel mayst thou wepe
>   and cryen."[1]

In spite of his sorrow, Mars patiently continues to follow
Venus, lamenting as he goes that his sphere is so large:

> "He passeth but oo steyre in dayes two,
> But ner the les, for al his hevy armure,
> He foloweth hir that is his lyves cure;[2]
>
> . . . .
>
> After he walketh softely a pas,
> Compleyning, that hit pite was to here.
> He seyde, 'O lady bright, Venus! alas!
> That ever so wyde a compass is my spere!
> Alas! whan shal I mete yow, herte dere,' " etc.[3]

Meanwhile Venus has passed on to Mercury's palace where
he soon overtakes her and receives her as his friend:[4]

>   "hit happed for to be,
> That, whyl that Venus weping made hir mone,
> Cylenius, ryding in his chevauche,
> Fro Venus valance mighte his paleys see,
> And Venus he salueth, and maketh chere,
> And hir receyveth as his frend ful dere."[5]

Mercury's palace was the sign Gemini and Venus' valance,
probably meaning her detrimentum or the sign opposite
her palace, was Aries. 'Chevauche' means an equestrian
journey or ride, and is here used in the sense of 'swift
course.' The passage, then, simply refers to the swift
motion by which in a very short time Mercury passes from
Aries to a position near enough to that of Venus in Gemini
so that he can see her and give her welcome. Mercury's

---

[1]*Ibid.* 98-112.
[2]That is, the motions of both planets are direct, not retrograde.
[3]*Ibid.* 129-138.
[4]*Ibid.* 142-147.
[5]That is, the two planets appear very close together in the sky.

sphere being the smallest of the planets, his motion is also the swiftest.

The size of Jupiter's orbit is not mentioned in Chaucer and that of Saturn's only once. In the *Knightes Tale* Saturn, addressing Venus, speaks of the great distance that he traverses with his revolving sphere but does not compare the size of his sphere with those of the other planets:

> " 'My dere doghter Venus,' quod Saturne,
> 'My cours, that hath so wyde for to turne,
> Hath more power than wot any man.' "[1]

Besides the reference in the *Compleynt of Mars* to the conjunction of Venus and Mars[2], there are occasional references in Chaucer to conjunctions of other planets. In the *Astrolabe*[3] Chaucer explains a method of determining in what position in the heavens a conjunction of the sun and moon takes place, when the time of the conjunction is known. A conjunction of the moon with Saturn and Jupiter is mentioned in *Troilus and Criseyde,* in the lines:

> "The bente mone with hir hornes pale,
> Saturne, and Iove, in Cancro ioyned were,"[4]

4. *The Galaxy*

The Galaxy or Milky Way, which stretches across the heavens like a broad band whitish in color caused by closely crowded stars, has appealed to men's imagination since very early times. Its resemblance to a road or street has been suggested in the names given to it by many peoples. Ovid called it *via lactea* and the Roman peasants, *strada di Roma;* pilgrims to Spain referred to it as the *road to Santiago;* Dante refers to it as "the white circle commonly

---

[1]*Knightes Tale,* A. 2453-5.
[2]71-72:
> "The grete Ioye that was betwix hem two,
> Whan they be met, ther may no tunge telle."
[3]II. 32.
[4]III. 624-5.

called St. Janus's Way"[1]; and the English had two names
for it, *Walsingham way* and *Watling-street.*

Chaucer twice mentions the Galaxy; once in the *Parlement of Foules,* where Africanus shows Scipio the location
of heaven by pointing to the Galaxy:

> "And rightful folk shal go, after they dye,
> To heven; and shewed him the galaxye."[2]

In the *Hous of Fame,* the golden eagle who bears Chaucer through the heavens toward Fame's palace, points
out to him the Galaxy and then relates the myth of Phaeton
driving the chariot of the sun, a story traditionally associated with the Milky Way:

> 'Now, 'quod he tho,' cast up thyn ye;
> See yonder, lo, the Galaxye,
> Which men clepeth the Milky Wey,
> For hit is whyt: and somme, parfey,
> Callen hit Watlinge Strete:
> That ones was y-brent with hete,
> Whan the sonnes sone, the rede,
> That highte Pheton, wolde lede
> Algate his fader cart, and gye.
> The cart-hors gonne wel espye
> That he ne coude no governaunce,
> And gonne for to lepe and launce,
> And beren him now up, now doun,
> Til that he saw the Scorpioun,
> Which that in heven a signe is yit.
> And he, for ferde, loste his wit,
> Of that, and lest the reynes goon
> Of his hors; and they anoon
> Gonne up to mounte, and doun descende
> Til bothe the eyr and erthe brende;
> Til Iupiter, lo, atte laste,
> Him slow, and fro the carte caste."[3]

In narrating this story here, Chaucer may have been imi-

[1]*Convivio,* II. xv. 10.
[2]255-56.
[3]*Hous of Fame,* II. 935-956.

tating Dante who refers to the myth in the *Divine Comedy*:

"What time abandoned Phaeton the reins,
Whereby the heavens, as still appears, were
scorched,"[1]

and states its source and the use made of it by some philosophers in the *Convivio*:

"For the Pythagoreans affirmed that the sun at one time wandered in its course, and in passing through other regions not suited to sustain its heat, set on fire the place through which it passed; and so these traces of the conflagration remain there. And I believe that they were influenced by the fable of Phaeton, which Ovid tells at the beginning of the second book of the *Metamorphoses*."[2]

V

ASTROLOGICAL LORE IN CHAUCER

Astrology, though resembling a science in that it makes use of observation and seeks to establish laws governing its data, is in reality a faith or creed. It had its beginning, so tradition tells us, in the faith of the ancient Babylonians in certain astral deities who exerted an influence upon terrestrial events and human life. The basis of this faith was not altogether illogical but contained a germ of truth.

Of all the heavenly bodies, the sun exerted the most obvious effect upon the earth; the sun brought day and night, summer and winter; his rays lured growing things from mother earth and so gave sustenance to mankind. But to the ancient peoples of the Orient the sun was also often a baneful power; he could destroy as well as give life. Therefore, the ancients came to look upon the sun as a great and powerful god to be worshipped and propitiated by men. And if the sun was such a power, it was natural to believe that all the other bright orbs of the sky were lesser div-

---

[1]*Inferno*, xvii. 107-108.
[2]*Convivio*, II. xv. 48-55.

inities who exercised more limited powers on the earth. From this beginning, based, as we have seen, on a germ of fact, by the power of his imagination and credulity, man extended more and more the powers of these sidereal divinities, attributing to their volition and influence all the most insignificant as well as the most important terrestrial events. And if the heavenly bodies, by revolving about the earth in ceaseless harmony, effected the recurrence of day and night and of the seasons, and if their configurations were responsible for the minutest events in nature, was it not natural to suppose that, besides affecting man thus indirectly, they also influenced him directly and were responsible for his conduct and for the very qualities of his mind and soul? Perhaps the astonishing variety of the influences that the celestial bodies, from ancient until modern times, were supposed to exercise over the world and the life of mankind can be accounted for by imagining some such process of thought to have been involved in the beginnings of astrology.

It was but a step from faith in stellar influence on our earth to the belief that, as the heavenly movements were governed by immutable laws, so their influence upon the world would follow certain laws and its effects in the future could be determined as certainly as could the coming revolutions and conjunctions of the stars. Out of this two-fold belief was evolved a complex system of divination, the origin of which was forgotten as men, believing in it, invented reasons for believing. pretending that their faith was founded on a long series of observations. The Chaldeans believed that in discovering the unceasing regularity of the celestial motions, they had found the very laws of life and they built upon this conviction a mass of absolutely rigid dogmas. But when experience belied these dogmas, unable to realize the falsity of their presuppositions and to give up their faith in the divine stars, the astrologers invented new dogmas to explain the old ones, thus piling up a body of complicated and often contradictory doctrines that will ever be to the student a source of perplexity and astonishment.

On its philosophical side astrology was a system of astral theology developed, not by popular thought, but through the careful observations and speculations of learned priests and scholars. It was a purely Eastern science which came into being on the Chaldean plains and in the Nile valley. As far as we know, it was entirely unknown to any of the primitive Aryan races, from Hindostan to Scandinavia. Astrology as a system of divination never gained a foothold in Greece during the brightest period of her intellectual life. But the dogma of astral divinity was zealously maintained by the greatest of Greek philosophers. Plato, the great idealist, whose influence upon the theology of the ancient and even of the modern world was more profound than that of any other thinker, called the stars "visible gods" ranking them just below the supreme eternal Being; and to Plato these celestial gods were infinitely superior to the anthropomorphic gods of the popular religion, who resembled men in their passions and were superior to them only in beauty of form and in power. Aristotle defended with no less zeal the doctrine of the divinity of the stars, seeing in them eternal substances, principles of movement, and therefore divine beings. In the Hellenistic period, Zeno, the Stoic, and his followers proclaimed the supremacy of the sidereal divinities even more strongly than the schools of Plato and Aristotle had done. The Stoics conceived the world as a great organism whose "sympathetic" forces constantly interacted upon one another, governed by Reason which was of the essence of ethereal Fire, the primordial substance of the universe. To the stars, the purest manifestation of the power of this ethereal substance, were attributed the greatest influence and the loftiest divine qualities. The Stoics developed the doctrine of fatalism, which is the inevitable outcome of faith in stellar influence on human life, to its consequences; yet they proved by facts that fatalism is not incompatible with active and virtuous living. By the end of the Roman imperial period astrology had transformed paganism, replacing the old society of Immortals who were scarcely superior to mortals, except in being exempted from old age and death, by faith in the eternal beings who ran their course in perfect harmony throughout the ages, whose power, regulated by the unvarying celestial motions, extended over all the earth and determined the destiny of the whole human race.

Astrology, as a science and a system of divination, exerted a profound influence over the mediaeval mind. No court was without its practicing astrologer and the universities all had their professors of astrology. The practice of astrology was an essential part of the physician's profession, and before prescribing for a patient it was thought quite as important to determine the positions of the planets as the nature of the disease.[1] Interesting evidence of this fact is found in the *Prologue to the Canterbury Tales* where Chaucer speaks of the Doctour's knowledge and use of astrology as if it were his chief excellence as a physician:

> "In al this world ne was ther noon him lyk
> To speke of phisik and of surgerye;
> For he was grounded in astronomye.
> He kepte his pacient a ful greet del
> In houres, by his magik naturel.
> Wel coude he fortunen the ascendent
> Of his images for his pacient."[2]

Yet in spite of the esteem in which astrological divination was held by most people in the Middle Ages, Dante, the greatest exponent of the thought and learning of that period, shows practically no knowledge of the technical and practical side of astrology. When he refers to the specific effects of the planets it is only to those most familiarly known, and he nowhere uses such technical terms as "houses" or "aspects" of planets. But Dante, like the great philosophers of the earlier periods, was undoubtedly in-

---

[1]Mrs. John Evershed, *Dante and the Early Astronomers*, p. 200.
[2]*Prologue to the Canterbury Tales*, A. 412-418.

fluenced by the philosophical doctrines of astrology, and a general belief in the influence of the celestial spheres upon human life was deeply rooted in his mind. To him the ceaseless and harmonious movements of the celestial bodies were the manifestations and instruments of God's providence, and were ordained by the First Mover to govern the destinies of the earth and human life.

We can see this conviction of Dante's with perfect certainty when we read the *Divina Commedia*. For Dante's poetry is highly subjective; on every page his own personal thoughts and feelings are revealed quite openly. Chaucer's poetry, on the other hand, is objective; he tells us almost nothing directly about himself and what we learn of him in his writings is almost entirely by inference. Chaucer's frequent use of astrology in his poetry would make it hard to believe that he was not considerably influenced by its philosophical aspects, at least in the general way that Dante was. Part and parcel of the dramatic action in most of his poems is the idea of stellar influences. Yet we cannot assert, with the same assurance that we can say it of Dante, that Chaucer believed, even in a general way, in the influence of the stars on human life. In Dante's poetry, as we have said, the poet himself is always before us. Chaucer, with Socratic irony, always makes it plain to the reader that his attitude is purely objective, that he is only the narrator of what he has seen or dreamed, only the copyist of another's story. Even when Chaucer makes himself one of the protagonists, as in the *Hous of Fame* and the *Canterbury Tales*, it is only that his narrative may be the more convincing. He tells a story and makes its protagonists actually live before us, as individual men and women. It is possible to imagine all of his use of astrology in his poetry not as the reflection of his own faith in its cosmic philosophy, but the expression of his genius for understanding people and truthfully describing life and character.

Considerable discussion as to Chaucer's attitude towards astrology has been called forth by passages in which

he speaks in words of scorn with regard to some of the
practices and magic arts that were often used in con-
nection with astrology. In the *Astrolabe* after describing
somewhat at length the favorable and unfavorable positions
of planets he says:

> "Natheles, thise ben observauncez of iudicial
> matiere and rytes of payens, in which my spirit
> ne hath no feith, ne no knowing of hir horos-
> copum."[1]

Again in the *Franklin's Tale* he speaks in a similar disdain-
ful tone of astrological magic:

> "He him remembred that, upon a day,
> At Orliens in studie a book he say
> Of magik naturel, which his felawe,
> That was that tyme a bacheler of lawe,
> Al were he ther to lerne another craft,
> Had prively upon his desk y-laft;
> Which book spak muchel of the operaciouns,
> Touchinge the eighte and twenty mansiouns
> That longen to the mone, and swich folye,
> As in our dayes is not worth a flye:
> For holy chirches feith in our bileve
> Ne suffreth noon illusion us to greve."[2]

And elsewhere in the same tale he writes:

> "So atte laste he hath his tyme y-founde
> To maken his Iapes and his wreccednesse
> Of switch a supersticious cursednesse."[3]

Here follows a long description of the clerk's instruments
and astrological observances, ending in the lines

> "For swiche illusiouns and swiche meschaunces
> As hethen folk used in thilke dayes;
> For which no lenger maked he delayes,
> But thurgh his magik, for a wyke or tweye,
> It seemed that alle the rokkes were aweye."[4]

---

[1] ii. 4. 36-39.
[2] F. 1123-34.
[3] F. 1270-72.
[4] F. 1285-96.

On the strength of these passages Professor T. R. Lounsbury[1] holds that Chaucer was far ahead of most of his contemporaries in his attitude toward the superstitious practices connected with the astrology of his day; that his attitude toward judicial astrology was one of total disbelief and scorn; and he even goes so far as to say that Chaucer was guilty of a breach of artistic workmanship in expressing his disbelief so scornfully in a tale in which the very climax of the dramatic action depends upon a feat of astrological magic.

A more satisfactory interpretation of the passages quoted above is advanced by Professor J. S. P. Tatlock,[2] who shows that Chaucer has taken great pains to place the setting of the *Franklin's Tale* in ancient times and that he, in common with most of the educated men of his day, disapproved of the practices (except sometimes when employed for good purposes as, e. g. in the physician's profession) and the practicians of judicial astrology in his own day, but thought of the feats and observances of astrological magic as having been possible and efficacious in ancient times. According to this view Chaucer's attitude was one of disapproval rather than disbelief, and his disapproval was not for the general theory of astrology, but for the shady observances and quackery connected with its application to the problems of life in his time. It is to be noted, further, that wherever Chaucer speaks in the strongest terms against astrological observances he also uses religious language. This fact may point to a wise caution on his part lest his evident interest in astrology, (which was closely associated with magic, and hence, indirectly, with sorcery) might involve him in difficulties with Mother Church; and, as Professor Tatlock has pointed out, there is no reason to suppose that Chaucer's religious expressions in these passages are insincere.

[1]*Studies in Chaucer*, vol. ii. 498, ff.
[2]"The Scene of *The Franklin's Tale* Visited," *Chaucer Society Publications*, (1914); "Astrology and Magic in Chaucer's *Franklin's Tale*;" *Kittredge Anniversary Papers* (1913).

The *Franklin's Tale* falls in the group of tales called by Professor Kittredge the "Marriage Group,"[1] that in which the Wife of Bath is the most conspicuous figure. The Wife of Bath's tale had aroused a rather heated controversy among a number of the Canterbury pilgrims on the subject of the respective duties and relations of wives and husbands. If the critics have been right in placing the *Franklin's Tale* where they do, it was Chaucer's purpose to have the Franklin soothe the ruffled feelings of certain members of the party by telling a tale in which a husband (and wife), a a squire, and a clerk, all prove themselves capable of truly generous behavior. If the tale was to accomplish its purpose the clerk must accomplish his magic feat of removing the rocks from the coast of Brittany, and must in the end generously refuse to accept pay from the squire when he learned that the latter had been too magnanimous to profit from his services. By setting the tale in pagan times, Chaucer was able to express the scorn he felt for certain superstitious practices in his own time without debasing one of his chief characters, one of the three rivals in magnanimity, and so spoiling the noble temper of the story and entirely defeating its purpose.

Thus the astrological passages in the *Franklin's Tale* do not suggest total disbelief in astrology on Chaucer's part, and much less do they show him to have been lacking in true artistic sense. Probably his attitude toward astrology was about this: he was very much interested in it, perhaps in much the same way that Dante was, because of the philosophical ideas at the basis of astrology and out of curiosity as to the problems of free will, providence, and so on, that naturally arose from it. For the shady practices and quackery connected with its use in his own day he had nothing but scorn.

But while Chaucer was at one with the educated men of his century in his attitude toward astrology, and with them had a strong distaste for certain aspects of judicial

---

[1] *Chaucer and His Poetry*, p. 186, ff.

astrology, nevertheless he made wide use of the greater faith of the majority of people of his time in portraying character in his poetry. For men's ideas and beliefs constitute a very important part of their character, and Chaucer knew this very well. Men believed that whatever happened to them, whether fortunate or unfortunate, could in some way be traced to the influence of the stars, the agents and instruments of destiny. The configuration of the heavens at the moment of one's birth was considered especially important, since the positions and interrelations of the different celestial bodies at this time could determine the most momentous events of one's life. Now the nature of the influence exerted by the different stars, especially the planets and zodiacal constellations, varied greatly. Mars and Venus, for instance, bestowed vastly different qualities upon the soul that was coming into being. Moreover, the power exerted by a planet or constellation fluctuated considerably according to its position. Each planet had in the zodiac a position of greatest and a position of least power called its "exaltation' and 'depression.' Furthermore, the 'aspect' or angular distance of one planet from another altered its influence in various ways. If Mars and Jupiter, for instance, were in trine or sextile aspect the portent was favorable, if in opposition, it was unfavorable.[1] These ideas are frequently expressed in Chaucer, when the characters seek to understand their misfortunes or to justify their conduct by tracing them back to the determinations of the heavens at their birth. When Palamon and Arcite have been thrown into prison the latter pleads with his companion to have patience; this misfortune was fixed upon them at the time of their birth by the disposition of the planets and constellations, and complaining is of no avail:

> " 'For Goddes love, tak al in pacience
> Our prisoun, for it may non other be;
> Fortune hath yeven us this adversitee.
> Som wikke aspect or disposicioun
> Of Saturne, by sum constellacioun

---

[1]The principal aspects were conjunction, sextile, quartile, trine, and opposition, corresponding respectively to the angular distances 0°, 60° 90°, 120° and 180°.

> Hath yeven us this, al-though we hadde it sworn;
> So stood the heven whan that we were born;
> We moste endure it: this is the short and pleyn.' "[1]

In the *Man of Lawes Tale* the effect of the stars at the time of a man's nativity is discussed somewhat at length. The Man of Law predicts the fate of the sultan by saying that the destiny written in the stars had perhaps allotted to him death through love:

> "Paraventure in thilke large book
> Which that men clepe the heven, y-writen was
> With sterres, whan that he his birthe took,
> That he for love shulde han his deeth, allas!
> For in the sterres, clerer than is glas,
> Is writen ,god wot, who-so coude it rede,
> The deeth of every man, withouten drede."[2]

Then he mentions the names of various ancient heroes whose death, he says was written in the stars "er they were born:"

> "In sterres, many a winter ther-biforn,
> Was written the deeth of Ector, Achilles,
> Of Pompey, Iulius, er they were born;
> The stryf of Thebes; and of Ercules,
> Of Sampson, Turnus, and of Socrates
> The deeth; but mennes wittes been so dulle,
> That no wight can wel rede it atte fulle."[3]

When Criseyde learns that she is to be sent to the Greeks in exchange for Antenor she attributes her misfortune to the stars:

> " 'Alas!' quod she, 'out of this regioun
> I, woful wrecche and infortuned wight,
> And born in corsed constellacioun,
> Mot goon, and thus departen fro my knight;' "[4]

---

[1]*Knightes Tale*, A. 1084-91.
[2]*Tale of the Man of Lawe*, B. 190-196.
[3]*Ibid.* 197-203.
[4]*Troilus and Criseyde*, IV. 743-746.

In the *Legend of Good Women* we are told that Hypermnestra was "born to all good things" or qualities, and then the various influences of the particular planets upon her destiny are mentioned:

"The whiche child, of hir nativitee,
 To alle gode thewes born was she,
 As lyked to the goddes, or she was born,
 That of the shefe she sholde be the corn;
 The Wirdes, that we clepen Destinee,
 Hath shapen her that she mot nedes be
 Pitouse, sadde, wyse, and trewe as steel;
 And to this woman hit accordeth weel.
 For, though that Venus yaf her great beautee,
 With Jupiter compouned so was she
 That conscience, trouthe, and dreed of shame,
 And of hir wyfhood for to keep her name,
 This, thoughte her, was felicitee as here.
 And rede Mars was, that tyme of the yere,
 So feble, that his malice is him raft,
 Repressed hath Venus his cruel craft;
 What with Venus and other oppressioun
 Of houses, Mars his venim is adoun,
 That Ypermistra dar nat handle a knyf
 In malice, thogh she sholde lese her lyf.
 But natheles ,as heven gan tho turne,
 To badde aspectes hath she of Saturne,
 That made her for to deyen in prisoun,
 As I shal after make mencioun."[1]

The purpose of this astrological passage is plainly to show why Hypermnestra was doomed to die in prison. The qualities given her by the planets, as shown by her horoscope, were such that she was unable to violate a wife's duty and kill her husband in order to save her own life.[2] Venus gave her great beauty and was also influential in repressing

---

[1] IX. 2576-2599.
[2] Her father, Egistes, because he feared her husband, bade her kill him by cutting his throat, and threatened her with death if she refused.

the influence of Mars who would have given her fighting
qualities if his influence had been strong. The myth of the
amour between Venus and Mars, which Chaucer makes the
basis of his poem the *Compleynt of Mars,* would explain
why Venus was able to influence Mars in this way. The
feeble influence of Mars at Hypermnestra's nativity is accounted for also in another way. His influence is feeble
because of the time of year and through the "oppressioun
of houses" both of which amount to the same thing, namely,
a position in the zodiac in which his power is at a min-
imum.[1] The influence of Jupiter, we are told,was to give
Hypermnestra conscience, truth, and wifely loyalty. That
of Saturn was evil and the cause of her death in prison.

The specific influences of Saturn are mentioned in detail in the *Knightes Tale.* Almost all the ills imaginable
are attributable to his power:

> " 'My dere doghter Venus,' quod Saturne,
> 'My cours, that hath so wyde for to turne,
> Hath more power than wot any man.
> Myn is the drenching in the see so wan;
> Myn is the prison in the derke cote;
> Myn is the strangling and hanging by the throte;
> The murmure, and the cherles rebelling,
> The groyning, and the pryvee empoysoning;
> I do vengeance and pleyn correccioun
> Whyl I dwelle in the signe of the leoun.
> Myn is the ruine of the hye halles,
> The falling of the toures and of the walles

---

[1]In astrology the signs of the zodiac were called 'houses' or 'mansions' and each was assigned to a particular planet. When a planet
was in its house or mansion, its power was very great. Each of the
planets had also a sign called its 'exaltation' and in this sign its power
was greatest of all. The sign opposite a planet's mansion was called
its 'fall' and that opposite its exaltation was called its 'depression';
these were the positions of least influence. Mars' mansions were Aries
and Scorpio; his exaltation, Capricornus; his fall, Libra and Taurus,
and his depression, Cancer. At the time of Hypermnestra's birth, then,
we may suppose that Mars was in Libra, Taurus or in Cancer. If he
was in Libra or Taurus, his influence would be suppressed by Venus,
as these signs were in her mansions.

> Up-on the mynour or the carpenter.
> I slow Sampsoun in shaking the piler;
> And myne be the maladyes colde,
> The derke tresons, and the castes olde;
> My loking is the fader of pestilence.' "[1]

In the line,

> "Myn is the prison in the derke cote;"

imprisonment is for the second time attributed to Saturn's influence. In an earlier passage in the *Knightes Tale*[2], (see p. 59) it is suggested when Palamon and Arcite's imprisonment is said to be due to 'some wicked aspect or disposition of Saturn' at the time of their birth. Later in the story Palamon specifically states that his imprisonment is through Saturn:

> "But I mot been in prison thurgh Saturne,"[3]

That Mars and Saturn were generally regarded as planets of evil influence is shown by a passage in the *Astrolabe*. Chaucer has just explained what the 'ascendant', means in astrology. It is that degree of the zodiac that at the given time is seen upon the eastern horizon. Now, Chaucer says, the ascendant may be 'fortunate or unfortunate,' thus:

> "a fortunat ascendent
> clepen they whan that no wykkid planete, as Saturne or Mars, or elles the Tail of the Dragoun, is in the house of the assendent, ne that no wikked planets have non aspects of enemite up-on the assendent;"[4]

The Wife of Bath attributes the two principal qualities of her disposition, amorousness and pugnaciousness, to the planets Venus and Mars:

[1]*Knightes Tale*, A. 2453-2469.
[2]*Ibid.* 1087-1088.
[3]*Ibid.* 1328.
[4]*Astrolabe*, ii. 4. 21-25. The term "hous" is here used in a different sense from that in the passage explained above. p. 120. The whole heavens were divided into twelve portions by great circles passing through the north and south points of the horizon. The one of these just rising was called the 'house of the ascendant.'

"For certes, I am al Venerien
In felinge, and myn herte is Marcien.
Venus me yaf my lust, my likerousnesse,
And Mars yaf me my sturdy hardinesse.
Myn ascendent was Taur, and Mars ther-inne.
Allas! allas! that ever love was sinne!
I folwed ay myn inclinacioun
By vertu of my constellacioun."[1]

A little later in her *Prologue* the Wife contrasts the influences of Mercury and Venus. As a jibe at the Clerk who was in the company of Canterbury pilgrims she has just said that clerks cannot possibly speak well of wives, and that women could tell tales of clerks if they would. She upholds her statement thus: Wives are the children of Venus, clerks, of Mercury, two planets that are 'in their working full contrarious:'

"The children of Mercurie and of Venus
Been in hir wirking ful contrarious;
Mercurie loveth wisdom and science,
And Venus loveth ryot and dispence.
And, for hir diverse disposicioun,
Ech falleth in otheres exaltacioun;
And thus, got woot! Mercurie is desolat
In Pisces, wher Venus is exaltat;
And Venus falleth ther Mercurie is reysed;
Therefore no womman of no clerk is preysed."[2]

Venus has her exaltation in the sign in which Mercury has his depression. Therefore the two signs have opposite virtues and influences, and the children of one can see little good in the children of the other.

We have seen how the stars were supposed to control human destiny by bestowing certain qualities upon souls at birth. We shall next consider how they were thought to

---

[1] *Wife of Bath's Prologue*, D. 609-616. The line
"Myn ascendent was Taur, and Mars ther-inne"
means that at the time of her birth Taurus was just rising in the east and Mars was in this sign, and as Taurus was the mansion of Venus, the influences of the two planets would be mingled.
[2] D. 697-706.

influence men more indirectly, through their effects on terrestrial events. Certain positions of the heavenly bodies with regard to one another could cause heavy rains. The clerk in the *Milleres Tale* predicts a great rain through observation of the moon's position:

> " 'Now John,' quod Nicholas, 'I wol nat lye;
> I have y-founde in myn astrologye,
> As I have loked in the mone bright,
> That now, a Monday next, at quarter-night,
> Shal falle a reyn and that so wilde and wood,
> That half so greet was never Noes flood.' "[1]

Such predictions as this were, however, by no means always believed in even by uneducated people. In this case, for the purposes of the story, the flood does not take place. The carpenter, John, is taken in because the story requires it, but Nicholas is a quack pure and simple, and of course the Miller who tells the story has no delusions.

In *Troilus and Criseyde* we are told that the moon's conjunction with Jupiter and Saturn caused a heavy rain. Pandarus had the day before suspected that there was to be rain from the condition of the moon:

> "Right sone upon the chaunging of the mone,
> Whan lightles is the world a night or tweyne,
> And that the welken shoop him for to reyne,
> He streight a-morwe un-to his nece wente;"[2]

and on the next night the rain came:

> "The bente mone with hir hornes pale,
> Saturne, and Iove, in Cancro ioyned were,
> That swich a rayn from hevene gan avale,
> That every maner womman that was there
> Hadde of that smoky reyn a verray fere;"[3]

Perhaps the moon alone in Cancer, which was her mansion, would have caused a rain, and it was the additional presence of Saturn and Jupiter that made it such a heavy downpour.

---

[1]A. 3513-3518.
[2]III. 549-552.
[3]III. 624-628.

Chaucer humorously makes use of this astrological superstition that the planets cause rains in the *Lenvoy a Scogan*:

> "To-broken been the statuts hye in hevene
> That creat were eternally to dure,
> Sith that I see the brighte goddes sevene
> Mow wepe and wayle, and passioun endure,
> As may in erthe a mortal creature.
> Allas, fro whennes may this thing procede?
> Of whiche errour I deye almost for drede."[1]

Here it is not the planets' positions that cause the rain, but the planets are weeping as mortals do and their tears are the rain. In the next stanza we learn that even Venus, from whose sphere divine law once decreed no tear should ever fall, is weeping so that mortals are about to be drenched. And it is all Scogan's fault!

> "By worde eterne whylom was hit shape
> That fro the fifte cercle, in no manere,
> Ne mighte a drope of teres doun escape.
> But now so wepeth Venus in hir spere,
> That with hir teres she wol drenche us here.
> Allas! Scogan! this is for thyn offence!
> Thou causest this deluge of pestilence."[2]

So the ultimate cause of the rain was Scogan's offense. And in the next stanza we learn what that offence was. Instead of vowing to serve his lady forever, though his love is unrequited, Scogan has rebelled against the law of love:

> "Hast thou not seyd, in blaspheme of this goddes,
> Through pryde, or through thy grete rakelnesse,
> Swich thing as in the lawe of love forbode is?
> That, for thy lady saw nat thy distresse,
> Therefor thou yave hir up at Michelmesse!"[3]

I have said that Chaucer makes wide use of the astro-logical beliefs of his century in portraying character and

---

[1] 1-7.
[2] 8-14.
[3] 15-19.

have shown how some of the strange astrological ideas of the people of his time are reflected in Chaucer's poetry. It remains to consider somewhat more closely the relations between astrological faith and conduct, and Chaucer's application of these relations to the dramatic action in his poems.

The inevitable logical outcome of astrological faith is the doctrine of Necessity. The invariability of the celestial motions suggested to early astrologers that there must be a higher power transcending and controlling them, and this power could be none other than Necessity. But, since the stars by their movements and positions were the regulators of mundane events and human affairs, it followed that human destiny on the earth was also under the sway of this relentless power of Necessity or Fate. Now it was the Stoics alone who developed a thorough-going fatalism and at the same time made it consistent with practical life and virtue. They taught that man could best find himself in complete submission to the divine law of destiny. The early Babylonian astrologers who originated the doctrine of necessity did not develop it to its logical consequences. Reasoning from certain very unusual occurrences that sometimes took place in the heavens, such as the appearance of comets, meteors and falling stars, they reached the conclusion that divine will at times arbitrarily interfered in the destined course of nature. So priests foretold future events from the configuration of the heavens, but professed ability to ward off threatened evils by spells and incantations, or, by purifications and sacrifices, to make the promised blessings more secure.

Now the fatalism of Chaucer's characters is something like this. The general belief in the determination of human destiny by Fortune or Necessity is present and is expressed usually at moments of deep despair, when the longings of the heart and the struggles of the will have been relentlessly thwarted. When the Trojans decree that Criseyde must go to the Greeks in exchange for Antenor, Troilus pleads with Fortune:

"Than seyde he thus, 'Fortune! allas the whyle!
What have I doon, what have I thus a-gilt?
How mightestow for reuthe me bigyle?
Is ther no grace, and shall I thus be spilt?
Shal thus Criseyde awey, for that thou wilt?
Allas! how maystow in thyn herte finde
To been to me thus cruel and unkinde?

. . . .

. . . .

. . . .

Allas! Fortune! if that my lyf in Ioye
Displesed hadde un-to thy foule envye,
Why ne haddestow my fader, king of Troye,
By-raft the lyf, or doon my bretheren dye,
Or slayn my-self, that thus compleyne and crye,
I, combre-world, that may of no-thing serve,
But ever dye, and never fulle sterve?' "[1]

But there is present, too, in spite of all obstacles and
defeats, an undying hope that somehow—by prayers and
sacrifices to the celestial powers, or by the choice of astro-
logically favorable times of doing things—that somehow the
course of human lives, mapped out at birth by the stars
under the control of relentless destiny, may be altered. So
the characters in Chaucer's poems pray to the orbs of the
sky to help in their undertakings. The love-lorn Troilus
undertakes scarcely a single act without first beseeching
some one of the celestial powers for help. When he has con-
fessed his love to Pandarus and the latter has promised to
help him, Troilus prays to Venus:

" 'Now blisful Venus helpe, er that I sterve,
    Of thee, Pandare, I may som thank deserve.' "[2]

and when the first step has been taken and he knows that
Criseyde is not ill disposed to be his friend at least, he
praises Venus, looking up to her as a flower to the sun:

[1]*Troilus and Criseyde,* IV. 260-266; 274-280.
[2]I. 1014-15.

"But right as floures, thorugh the colde of night
Y-closed, stoupen on hir stalkes lowe,
Redressen hem a-yein the sonne bright,
And spreden on hir kinde cours by rowe;
Right so gan tho his eyen up to throwe
This Troilus, and seyde, 'O Venus dere,
Thy might, thy grace, y-heried be it here!' "[1]

When Troilus is about to undertake a step that will either win or lose Criseyde he prays to all the planetary gods, but especially to Venus, begging her to overcome by her aid whatever evil influences the planets exercised over him in his birth:

" 'Yit blisful Venus, this night thou me enspyre,'
Quod Troilus, 'as wis as I thee serve,
And ever bet and bet shal, til I sterve.
And if I hadde, O Venus ful of murthe,
Aspectes badde of Mars or of Saturne,
Or thou combust[2] or let were in my birthe,
Thy fader prey al thilke harm disturne.' "[3]

Troilus does not forget to praise Venus when Criseyde is won at last:

"Than seyde he thus, 'O, Love, O, Charitee,
Thy moder eek, Citherea the swete,
After thy-self next heried be she,
Venus mene I, the wel-willy planete;' "[4]

And after Criseyde has gone away to the Greeks, it is to Venus still that the lover utters his lament and prayer, saying that without the guidance of her beams he is lost:

---

[1] II. 967-973.

[2] A planet was said to be *combust* when its light was extinguished by proximity to the sun. When Venus and Mercury were 'combust' their influence was lost.

[3] III. 712-718 . It is sometimes hard to determine whether the beings prayed to are pagan gods and goddesses or heavenly bodies. This passage makes it clear that the planets were identified with the pagan divinities. In the rest of this prayer Troilus addresses Mars, Mercury, Jupiter, etc., as gods, referring in each case to some love affair, from ancient myth, that may win the god's sympathy and help.

[4] III. 1254-1257. The "wel-willy planete" means the propitious or favorable one.

" 'O sterre, of which I lost have al the light,
With herte soor wel oughte I to bewayle,
That ever derk in torment, night by night,
Toward my deeth with wind in stere I sayle;
For which the tenthe night if that I fayle
The gyding of thy bemes brighte an houre,
My ship and me Caribdis wol devoure:' "[1]

Another effect of astrological faith on conduct was the choice of times for doing things of importance with reference to astrological conditions. When a man wished to set out on any enterprise of importance he very often consulted the positions of the stars to see if the time was propitious. Thus in the *Squieres Tale* it is said that the maker of the horse of brass

> "wayted many a constellacioun,
> Er he had doon this operacioun;"[2]

that is, he waited carefully for the moment when the stars would be in the most propitious position, so that his undertaking would have the greatest possible chance of success. Pandarus goes to his niece Criseyde to plead for Troilus at a time when the moon is favorably situated in the heavens:

> "And gan to calle, and dresse him up to ryse,
> Remembringe him his erand was to done
> From Troilus, and eek his greet empryse;
> And caste and knew in good plyt was the mone—
> To doon viage, and took his wey ful sone
> Un-to his neces paleys ther bi-syde."[3]

The kind of fatalism that Chaucer's characters, as a rule, represent is well illustrated in the story of Palamon and Arcite, told by the Knight in the *Canterbury Tales*. These two young nobles of Thebes, cousins by relationship, are captured by Theseus, king of Athens, and imprisoned in the tower of his palace. From the window of the tower

---

[1] V. 638-644. Troilus needs the aid of Venus especially on the tenth night after Criseyde's departure, because she had promised to return on that night.
[2] F. 129-130.
[3] II. 71-76.

Palamon espies the king's beautiful sister Emelye walking
in the garden and instantly falls in love. Arcite, seeing
his cousin's sudden pallor and hearing his exclamation
which, Chaucer says, sounded

"As though he stongen were un-to the herte."[1]
thinks that Palamon is complaining because of his imprisonment and urges him to bear in patience the decree of the
heavens:

> " 'For Goddes love, tak al in pacience
> Our prisoun, for it may non other be;
> Fortune hath yeven us this adversitee.
> Som wikke aspect or disposicioun
> Of Saturne, by sum constellacioun,
> Hath yeven us this, al-though we hadde it sworn;
> So stood the heven whan that we were born;
> We moste endure it; this is the short and pleyn.' "[2]

This is the doctrine of Necessity, and it suggests the
Stoic virtue of submission to fate; yet Arcite's attitude to-
word his misfortune is not truly stoic, for there is none of
that joy in submission here that the Stoic felt in surrender-
ing himself to the will of the powers above. Arcite would
resist fate if he could.

Palamon explains the cause of his woe and when Arcite
looks out and sees Emelye he too falls a victim to love. Then
Palamon knits his brows in righteous indignation. Did he
not love the beautiful lady first and trust his secret to his
cousin and sworn brother? And was it not Arcite's duty
and solemn pledge to help and not hinder him in his love?
Arcite's defence shows that the fatalism that dominates his
thought is a fatalism that excuses him for doing as he
pleases: Love knows no law, but is a law unto itself. Therefore he must needs love Emelye.

> "Wostow nat wel the olde clerkes sawe,
> That 'who shal yeve a lover any lawe?'
> Love is a gretter lawe, by my pan,

---

[1]*Knightes Tale*, A. 1079.
[2]*Ibid.* 1084-1091.

Than may be yeve to any erthly man.
And therefore positif lawe and swich decree
Is broke al-day for love, in ech degree.
A man moot nedes love, maugree his heed."[1]

When Arcite is released from prison but banished from Athens with the threat of death should he return, both men are utterly unhappy, Arcite, because he can no longer see Emelye, and Palamon because he fears that Arcite will return to Athens with a band of kinsmen to aid him, and carry off Emelye by force.　After Arcite has gone Palamon reproaches the gods for determining the destiny of men so irrevocably without consulting their wishes or their deserts:

" 'O cruel goddes, that governe
This world with binding of your word eterne,
And wryten in the table of athamaunt
Your parlement, and your eterne graunt,
What is mankinde more un-to yow holde
Than is the sheep, that rouketh in the folde?' "[2]

Many a man, Palamon says, suffers sickness, imprisonment and other misfortunes unjustly because of the inexorable destiny imposed upon him by the gods.　Even the lot of the beasts is better, for they do as they will and have nothing to suffer for it after death; whereas man must suffer both in this life and the next.　This, surely, is not willing submission to fate.

After some years Palamon escapes from prison and encounters Arcite, who has returned in disguise and become Theseus' chief squire.　They arrange to settle their differences by a duel next day.　But destiny was guiding Theseus' conduct too, so the narrator of the story says, and was so powerful that it caused a coincidence that might not happen again in a thousand years:

"The destinee, ministre general,
That executeth in the world over-al

---

[1]A. 1163-69.
[2]A. 1303-8.

The purveyaunce, that God hath seyn biforn,
So strong it is, that, though the world had sworn
The contrarie of a thing, by ye or nay,
Yet somtyme it shal fallen on a day
That falleth nat eft with-inne a thousand yere.
For certeinly, our appetytes here,
Be it of werre, or pees, or hate, or love,
Al is this reuled by the sighte above."[1]

Theseus goes hunting and with him, the queen and
Emelye. They of course interrupt the duel between Palamon and Arcite. Through the intercession of the two
women the duelists are pardoned and it is arranged that
they settle their dispute by a tournament set for about a
year later.

On the morning before the tournament Palamon, Arcite,
and Emelye all go, at different hours, to pray and sacrifice to
their respective patron deities. The times of their prayers
are chosen according to astrological considerations, each
going to pray in the hour[2] that was considered sacred to
the planet with which his patron deity was identified. Palamon prays to Venus only that he may win his love, whether
by victory or defeat in the tournament makes no difference
to him. After his sacrifices are completed, the statute of
Venus shakes and Palamon, regarding this as a favorable
sign goes away with glad heart. Arcite prays Mars for victory and is answered by a portent even more favorable than
that given to Palamon. Not only does the statue of Mars
tremble so that his coat of mail resounds, but the very doors
of the temple shake, the fire on the altar burns more brightly
and Arcite hears the word "Victory" uttered in a low dim
murmur. Emelye does not want to be given in marriage
to any man and so she prays to Diana[3], as the protectress of

---

[1]A. 1663-1672. This is the mediaeval Christian idea of destiny or
the fore-knowledge of God, and is appropriately uttered here by the
Knight.

[2]A. 2209 ff; 2271 ff; 2367 ff.

[3]Diana was called *Luna* (or the Moon) in heaven, on earth, *Diana*
or *Lucina*, and in hell, *Proserpina*.

maidenhood, to keep her a maid. Diana, the goddess, appears in her characteristic form as a huntress and tells Emelye that the gods have decreed her marriage either to Palamon or to Arcite, but that it cannot yet be revealed to which one she is to be given.

But now there is trouble in heaven. Venus has promised that Palamon shall have his love, and Mars has promised Arcite the victory. How are both promises to be fulfilled? Chaucer humorously expresses the dilemma thus:

> "And richt anon swich stryf ther is bigonne
> For thilke graunting, in the hevene above,
> Bitwixe Venus, the goddesse of love,
> And Mars, the sterne god armipotente,
> That Iupiter was bisy it to stente;
> Til that the pale Saturnus the colde,
> That knew so manye of aventures olde,
> Fond in his old experience an art,
> That he ful sone hath plesed every part."[1]

We had almost forgotten that all the gods to whom prayers have been uttered and sacrifices offered were anything more than pagan gods. But now, by the reference to Saturn, "the pale Saturnus the colde" suggesting the dimness of his appearance in the sky, we are reminded that these gods are also planets.

But, to resume the story, Saturn finds the remedy for the embarrassing situation. He rehearses his powers and then tells Venus that her knight shall have his lady, but that Mars shall be able to help his knight also.

> " 'My dere doghter Venus,' quod Saturne,
> 'My cours, that hath so wyde for to turne,
> Hath more power that wot any man.
>
> .   .   .   .
>
> Now weep namore, I shal doon diligence
> That Palamon, that is thyn owne knight,
> Shal have his lady, as thou hast him hight.

---

[1]A. 2438-2446.

Though Mars shal helpe his knight, yet nathelees
Bitwixe yow ther moot be som tyme pees,
Al be ye noght of o complexioun,
That causeth al day swich divisioun.' "[1]

When the appointed time for the tourney arrives, in
order that no means of securing the god's favor and so
assuring success may be left untried, Arcite, with his
knights, enters through the gate of Mars, his patron deity,
and Palamon through that of Venus. Palamon is defeated
in the fight but Saturn fulfills his promise to Venus by in-
ducing Pluto to send an omen which frightens Arcite's horse
causing an accident in which Arcite is mortally injured.
In the end Palamon wins Emelye.

Although the scene of this story is laid in ancient
Athens, the characters are plainly mediaeval knights and
ladies. Throughout the poem, as in many of Chaucer's
writings, there is a curious mingling of pagan and Christian
elements, a strange juxtaposition of astrological notions,
Greek anthropomorphism and mediaeval Christian philosophy. But pervading the whole is the idea of determin-
ism, of the inability of the human will to struggle success-
fully against the destiny imposed by the powers of heaven,
or against the capricious wills of the gods.

Chaucer had too keen a sense of humor, too sympathetic
an outlook on life not to see the irony in the ceaseless
spectacle of mankind dashing itself against the relentless
wall of circumstances, fate, or what you will, in undying
hope of attaining the unattainable. He saw the humor in
this maelstrom of human endeavor—and he saw the tragedy
too. The *Knightes Tale* presents largely, I think, the humorous side of it, *Troilus and Criseyde*, the tragic, although
there is some tragedy in the *Knightes Tale* and some comedy
in *Troilus*.

It was fate that Troilus should love Criseyde, that he
should win her love for a time, and that in the end he

[1]A. 2453-2455; 2470-2476.

should be deserted by her. From the very first line of the poem we know that he is doomed to sorrow:

"The double sorwe of Troilus to tellen,
That was the king Priamus sone of Troye,
In lovinge, how his aventures fellen
Fro wo to wele, and after out of Ioye,
My purpos is, er that I parte fro ye."[1]

The tragedy of Troilus is also the tragedy of Criseyde, for even at the moment of forsaking Troilus for Diomede she is deeply unhappy over her unfaithfulness; but circumstance is as much to blame as her own yielding nature, for Troilus' fate is bound up with the inexorable doom of Troy, and she could not return to him if she would.

There is no doubt that Chaucer feels the tragedy of the story as he writes. In his proem to the first book he invokes one of the furies to aid him in his task:

"Thesiphone, thou help me for tendyte
Thise woful vers, that wepen as I wryte!"[2]

Throughout the poem he disclaims responsibility for what he narrates, saying that he is simply following his author and that, once begun, somehow he must keep on. In the proem to the second book he says:

"Wherefore I nil have neither thank ne blame
Of al this werk, but pray you mekely,
Disblameth me, if any word be lame,
For as myn auctor seyde, so seye I."[3]

and concludes the proem with the words,—

"but sin I have begonne,
Myn auctor shal I folwen, if I conne."[4]

When Fortune turns her face away from Troilus, and Chaucer must tell of the loss of Criseyde his heart bleeds and his pen trembles with dread of what he must write:

"But al to litel, weylawey the whyle,
Lasteth swich Ioye, y-thonked be Fortune!

---

[1]*Troilus and Criseyde*, I. 1-5.
[2]*Ibid.* I. 6-7.
[3]II.   15-18.
[4]II.   48-49.

That semeth trewest, whan she wol bygyle,
And can to foles so hir song entune,
That she hem hent and blent, traytour comune;
And whan a wight is from hir wheel y-throwe,
Than laugheth she, and maketh him the mowe.

From Troilus she gan hir brighte face
Awey to wrythe, and took of him non hede,
But caste him clene oute of his lady grace,
And on hir wheel she sette up Diomede;
For which right now myn herte ginneth blede,
And now my penne, allas! with which I wryte,
Quaketh for drede of that I moot endyte."[1]

Chaucer tells of Criseyde's faithlessness reluctantly, reminding the reader often that so the story has it:

"And after this the story telleth us,
That she him yaf the faire baye stede,
The which she ones wan of Troilus;
And eek a broche (and that was litel nede)
That Troilus was, she yaf this Diomede.
And eek, the bet from sorwe him to releve,
She made him were a pencel of hir sleve.

I finde eek in the stories elles-where,
Whan through the body hurt was Diomede
Of Troilus, tho weep she many a tere,
Whan that she saugh his wyde woundes blede;
And that he took to kepen him good hede,
And for to hele him of his sorwes smerte,
Men seyn, I not, that she yaf him hir herte."[2]

And in the end for very pity he tries to excuse her:

"Ne me ne list this sely womman chyde
Ferther than the story wol devyse,
Hir name, allas! is publisshed so wyde,
That for hir gilt it oughte y-now suffyse.
And if I mighte excuse hir any wyse,

[1]IV. 1-14.
[2]V. 1037-1050.

> For she so sory was for hir untrouthe,
> Y-wis, I wolde excuse hir yet for routhe."[1]

We have said that Chaucer's attitude toward the philosophical aspects of astrology is hard to determine because in most of his poems he takes an impersonal ironic point of view towards the actions he describes or the ideas he presents. His attitude toward the idea of destiny is not so hard to determine. Fortune, the executrix of the fates through the influence of the heavens rules men's lives; they are the herdsmen, we are their flocks:

> "But O, Fortune, executrice of wierdes,
> O influences of thise hevenes hye!
> Soth is, that, under god, ye ben our hierdes,
> Though to us bestes been the causes wrye."[2]

Perhaps Chaucer did not mean this literally. But one is tempted to think that he, like Dante, thought of the heavenly bodies in their spheres as the ministers and instruments of a Providence that had foreseen and ordained all things.

---

[1]V. 1093-1099.
[2]*Troilus and Criseyde*, III. 617-620.

APPENDIX

I. Most of the terms at present used to describe the movements of the heavenly bodies were used in Chaucer's time and occur very frequently in his writings. The significance of Chaucer's references will then be perfectly clear, if we keep in mind that the modern astronomer's description of the *apparent* movements of the star-sphere and of the heavenly bodies individually would have been to Chaucer a description of *real* movements.

When we look up into the sky on a clear night the stars and planets appear to be a host of bright dots on the concave surface, unimaginably distant, of a vast hollow sphere at the center of which we seem to be. Astronomers call this expanse of the heavens with its myriad bright stars the *celestial sphere* or the *star sphere,* and have imagined upon its surface various systems of circles. In descriptions of the earth's relation to the celestial sphere it is customary to disregard altogether the earth's diameter which is comparatively infinitesimal.

If we stand on a high spot in the open country and look about us in all directions the earth seems to meet the sky in a circle which we call the *terrestrial horizon.* Now if we imagine a plane passing through the center of the earth and parallel to the plane in which the terrestrial horizon lies, and if we imagine this plane through the earth's center extended outward in all directions to an infinite distance, it would cut the celestial sphere in a great circle which astronomers call the *celestial horizon.* On the celestial horizon are the north, east, south and west points. The plane of the celestial horizon is, of course, different for different positions of the observer on the earth.

If we watch the sky for some time, or make several observations on the same night, we notice, by observing the changing positions of the constellations, that the stars move very slowly across the blue dome above us. The stars that rise due east of us do not, in crossing the dome of the sky, pass directly over our heads but, from the moment that we first see them, curve some distance to the south, and, after passing their highest point in the heavens, turn toward the north and set due west. A star rising due east appears to move more rapidly than one rising some distance to the north or south of the east point, because it crosses a higher point in the heavens and has, therefore, a greater distance to traverse in the same length of time. When we observe the stars in the northern sky, we discover that many of them never set but seem to be moving around an apparently fixed point at somewhat more than an angle of 40°[1] above the northern horizon and very near the north star. These are called

---

[1]For Chaucer's locality, 45°.

circum-polar stars. The whole celestial sphere, in other words, appears to be revolving about an imaginary axis passing through this fixed point, which is called the *north pole* of the heavens, through the center of the earth and through an invisible pole (the south pole of the heavens) exactly opposite the visible one. This apparent revolution of the whole star sphere, as we know, is caused by the earth's rotation on its axis once every twenty-four hours from west to east. Chaucer and his contemporaries believed it to be the actual revolution of the nine spheres from east to west about the earth as a center.

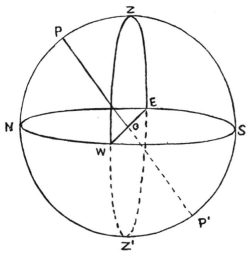

Fig. 1

For determining accurately the position of stars on the celestial sphere astronomers make use of various circles which can be made clear by a few simple diagrams. In Figure 1, the observer is imagined to be at 0. Then the circle NESW is the celestial horizon, which we have described above. Z, the point immediately above the observer is called the *zenith*, and Z', the point immediately underneath, as indicated by a plumb line at rest, is the *nadir*. The line POP' is the imaginary axis about which the star-sphere appears to revolve, and P and P' are the poles of the heavens. The north pole P is elevated, for our latitude, at an angle of approximately 40° from the north point on the horizon. PP' is called the *polar axis* and it is evident that the earth's axis extended infinitely would coincide with this axis of the heavens.

In measuring positions of stars with reference to the horizon astronomers use the following circles: Any great circle of the celestial sphere whose plane passes through the zenith and nadir is called a *vertical circle*. The verticle circle SPNZ', passing through the poles and meeting the horizon in the north and south points, N and S, is called the *meridian circle*, because the sun is on this circle at true mid-day. The *meridian* is the plane in which this circle lies. The vertical circle, EZ'WZ, whose plane is at right angles to the meridian, is called the *prime vertical* and it intersects the horizon at the east and west points, E and W. These circles, and the measurements of positions of heavenly bodies which involve their use, were all employed in Chaucer's time and are referred to in his writings.[1]

The distance of a star from the horizon, measured on a vertical circle, toward the zenith is called the star's *altitude*. A star reaches its greatest altitude when on the part of the meridional circle between the south point of the horizon, S, and the north pole, P. A star seen between the north pole and the north point on the horizon, that is, on the arc PN, must obviously be a *circum-polar star* and would have its highest altitude when between the pole and the zenith, or on the arc PZ. When a star reaches the meridian in its course across the celestial sphere it is said to *culminate* or reach its *culmination*. The highest altitude of any star would therefore be represented by the arc of the meridional circle between the star and the south point of the horizon. This is called the star's *meridian altitude*.

The *azimuth* of a star is its angular distance from the south point, measured westward on the horizon, to a vertical circle passing through the star. The *amplitude* of a star is its distance from the prime vertical, measured on the horizon, north or south.

For the other measurements used by astronomers in observations of the stars still other circles on the celestial sphere must be imagined. We know that the earth's surface is divided into halves, called the northern and southern hemispheres, by an imaginary circle called the *equator*, whose plane passes through the center of the earth and is perpendicular to the earth's axis. If the plane of the earth's equator were infinitely extended it would describe upon the celestial sphere a great circle which would divide that sphere into two hemispheres, just as the plane of the terrestrial equator divides the earth into two hemispheres. This great circle on the celestial sphere is called the *celestial equator*, or, by an older name, the *equatorial*, the significance of which we shall see presently. A star rising due east would traverse this great circle of the celestial sphere and set due west. The path of such a star is represented in Figure 2 by the great circle EMWM', which also represents the celestial equator. All stars rise and set following circles whose planes are parallel to that of the

1. See the *Astrolabe*, i. 18, 19. Vertical circles are called *azimuths* by Chaucer.

celestial equator and these circles of the celestial sphere are smaller and smaller the nearer they are to the pole, so that stars very near the pole appear to be encircling it in very small concentric circles. Stars in an area around the north celestial pole, whose limits vary with the position of the observer never set for an observer in the northern hemisphere. There is a similar group of stars around the south pole for an observer in the southern hemisphere.

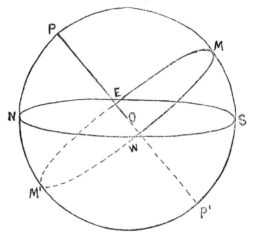

Fig. 2.

The angle of elevation of the celestial equator to the horizon varies according to the position of the observer. If, for example, the observer were at the north pole of the earth, the north celestial pole would be directly above him and would therefore coincide with the zenith; this would obviously make the celestial equator and the horizon also coincide. If the observer should pass slowly from the pole to the terrestrial equator it is clear that the two circles would no longer coincide and that the angle between them would gradually widen until it reached 90°. Then the zenith would be on the celestial equator and the north and south poles of the heavens would be on the horizon.

We have still to define a great circle of the celestial sphere that is of equal importance with the celestial equator and the celestial horizon. This is the sun's apparent yearly path, or the *ecliptic*. We know that the earth revolves about the sun once yearly in an orbit that is not entirely round but somewhat eliptical. Now since the earth, the sun, and the earth's orbit around the sun are always in **one plane**, it follows that to an observer on the earth the sun would appear to be moving around the earth instead of the earth around the sun. The sun's apparent path, moreover, would be in the plane of the earth's orbit and when projected against the celestial sphere, which is infinite in extent, would appear as a great circle of that sphere. This great circle of the celestial sphere is the ecliptic. The sun must always appear to be on this circle, not only at all times of the year but at all hours of the day; for as the sun rises and sets, the ecliptic rises and sets also, since the earth's rotation causes an apparent daily revolution not only of the sun, moon, and planets but also of the fixed stars and so of the whole celestial sphere and of all the circles whose positions upon it do not vary. The ecliptic is inclined to the celestial equator approximately 23½°, an angle which obviously measures the inclination of the plane of the earth's equator to the plane of its orbit, since the celestial equator and the ecliptic are great circles on the celestial sphere formed by extending the planes of the earth's equator and its orbit to an infinite distance. Since both the celestial equator and the ecliptic are great circles of the celestial sphere each dividing it into equal parts, it is evident that these two circles must intersect at points exactly opposite each other on the celestial sphere. These points are called the vernal and the autumnal equinoxes.

We shall next define the astronomical measurements that correspond to terrestrial latitude and longitude. For some reason astronomers have not, as we might expect, applied to these measurements the terms 'celestial longitude' and 'celestial latitude.' These two terms are now practically obsolete, having been used formerly to denote angular distance north or south of the ecliptic and angular distance measured east and west along circles parallel to the celiptic. The measurements that correspond in astronomy to terrestrial latitude and longitude are called *declination* and *right ascension* and are obviously made with reference to the celestial equator, not the ecliptic. For taking these measurements astronomers employ circles on the celestial sphere perpendicular to the plane of the celestial equator and passing through the poles of the heavens. These are called *hour circles*. The hour circle of any star is the great circle passing through it and perpendicular to the plane of the equator. The angular distance of a star from the equator measured along its hour circle, is called the star's declination and is northern or southern according as the star is in the northern or southern of the two hemispheres into which the plane of the equator divides the celestial sphere. It is evident that declination corresponds exactly to terrestrial latitude. Right ascension, corresponding to terrestrial longitude, is the angular distance of a heavenly body from the vernal equinox measured on the celestial equator eastward to the hour circle passing through the body.

The *hour angle* of a star is the angular distance measured on the celestial equator from the meridian to the foot of the hour circle passing through the star.

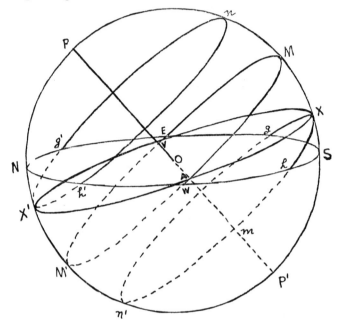

Fig. 3.

It remains to describe in greater detail the apparent movements of the sun and the sun's effect upon the seasons. In Figure 3, the great circle MWM'E represents the equinoctial and XVX'A the ecliptic. The point X represents the farthest point south that the sun reaches in its apparent journey around the earth, and this point is called the *winter solstice*, because, for the northern hemisphere the sun reaches this point in mid-winter. When the sun is south of the celestial equator its apparent daily path is the same as it would be for a star so situated. Thus its daily path at the time of the winter solstice, about December 21, can be represented by the circle Xmn'. The arc gXh represents the part of the sun's path that would be above the horizon, showing that night would last much longer than day and the rays of the sun would strike the northern hemisphere of the earth more indirectly than when the sun is north of the equator. As the sun passes along the ecliptic from X toward V, the part of its daily path that is above the horizon gradually increases until at V, the vernal equinox, the sun's path would, roughly speaking, coincide with the celestial equator so that half of it would be above the horizon and half below and day and night would be of equal length. This explains why the celestial equator was formerly called the equinoctial (Chaucer's term for it). As the sun passes on toward X' its daily arc continues to increase and the days to grow longer until at X' it reaches its greatest declination north of the equator and we have the longest day, June 21, the summer solstice. When the sun reaches this point, its rays strike the northern hemisphere more directly than at any other time causing the hot or summer season in this hemisphere. Next the sun's daily arc begins to decrease, day and night to become more nearly equal, at A the autumnal equinox[1] is reached and the sun again shapes its course towards the point of maximum declination south of the equator. The two points of maximum declination are called *solstices*.

The two small circles of the celestial sphere, parallel to the equator, which pass through the two points where the sun's declination is greatest, are called *Tropics*; the one in the northern hemisphere is called the *Tropic of Cancer*, that in the southern hemisphere, the *Tropic of Capricorn*. They correspond to circles on the earth's surface having the same names.

II. By "artificial day" Chaucer means the time during which the sun is above the horizon, the period from sunrise to sunset. The arc of the artificial day may mean the extent or duration of it, as measured on the rim of an astrolabe, or it may mean (as here), the arc extending from the point of sunrise to that of sunset. See *Astrolabe* ii.7.

There has been some controversy among editors as to the correctness of the date occurring in this passage, some giving it as the 28th instead of the 18th. In discussing the accuracy of the reading "eightetethe" Skeat throws light also upon the accuracy of the rest of the passage considered from an astronomical point of view. He says (vol. 5, p. 133):

"The key to the whole matter is given by a passage in Chaucer's 'Astrolabe,' pt. ii, ch. 29, where it is clear that Chaucer (who, however merely translates from Messahala) actually confuses the hour-angle with the azimuthal arc (see Appendix I); that is, he considered it correct to find the hour of the day by noting *the point of the horizon* over which the sun appears to stand, and supposing this point to advance, with a *uniform*, not a *variable*, motion. The host's method of proceeding was this. Wanting to know the hour, he observed how far the sun had moved southward along the

---

[1]Strictly speaking, the equinoxes and solstices are each simply an instant of time.

horizon since it rose, and saw that it had gone more than half-way from the point of sunrise to the exact southern point. Now the 18th of April in Chaucer's time answers to the 26th of April at present. On April 26, 1874, the sun rose at 4 hr. 43 m., and set at 7 hr. 12 m., giving a day of about 14 hr. 30 m., the fourth part of which is at 8 hr. 20 m., or, with sufficient exactness, at *half past eight.* This would leave a whole hour and a half to signify Chaucer's 'half an houre and more', showing that further explanation is still necessary. The fact is, however, that the host reckoned, as has been said, in another way, viz. by observing the sun's position *with reference to the horizon.* On April 18 the sun was in the 6th degree of Taurus at that date, as we again learn from Chaucer's treatise. Set this 6th degree of Taurus on the east horizon on a globe, and it is found to be 22 degrees to the north of the east point, or 112 degrees from the south. The half of this at 56 degrees from the south; and the sun would seem to stand above this 56th degree, as may be seen even upon a globe, at about a quarter past nine; but Mr. Brae has made the calculation, and shows that it was at *twenty minutes past nine.* This makes Chaucer's 'half an houre and more' to stand for *half an hour and ten minutes;* an extremely neat result. But this we can check again by help of the host's *other* observation. He *also* took note, that the lengths of a shadow and its object were equal, whence the sun's altitude must have been 45 degrees. Even a globe will shew that the sun's altitude, when in the 6th degree of Taurus, and at 10 o'clock in the morning, is somewhere about 45 or 46 degrees. But Mr. Brae has calculated it exactly, and his result is, that the sun attained its altitude of 45 degrees at *two minutes to ten* exactly. This is even a closer approximation than we might expect, and leaves no doubt about the right date being the *eighteenth* of April."

Thus it appears that Chaucer's method of determining the date was incorrect but his calculations in observing the sun's position were quite accurate. For fuller particulars see Chaucer's *Astrolabe,* ed. Skeat (E. E. T. S.) preface, p. 1.

III. It was customary in ancient times and even as late as Chaucer's century to determine the position of the sun, moon, or planets at any time by reference to the signs of the zodiac. The *zodiac* is an imaginary belt of the celestial sphere, extending 8° on each side of the ecliptic, within which the orbits of the sun, moon, and planets appear to lie. The zodiac is divided into twelve equal geometric divisions 30° in extent called *signs* to each of which a fanciful name is given. The signs were once identical with twelve constellations along the zodiac to which these fanciful names were first applied. Since the signs are purely geometric divisions and are counted from the spring equinox in the direction of the sun's progress through them, and since through the precession of the equinoxes the whole series of signs shifts westward about one degree in seventy-two years, the signs and constellations no longer coincide. Beginning with the sign in which the vernal equinox lies the names of the zodiacal signs are Aries (Ram), Taurus (Bull), Gemini (Twins), Cancer (Crab), Leo (Lion), Virgo (Virgin), Libra (Scales), Scorpio (Scorpion), Sagittarius (Archer), Aquarius (Water-carrier), and Pisces (Fishes).

In this passage, the line "That in the Ram is four degrees upronne" indicates the date March 16. This can be seen by reference to Figure 1 in Skeat's edition of Chaucer's *Astrolabe* (E. E. T. S.) The astrolabe was an instrument for making observations of the heavenly bodies and calculating time from these observations. The most important part of the kind of astrolabe described by Chaucer was a rather heavy circular plate of metal from four to seven inches in diameter, which could be suspended from the thumb by a ring attached loosely enough so as to allow the instrument to assume a perpendicular position. One side of this plate was flat and was called the *back*, and it is this part that Figure 1 represents. The back of the astrolabe planisphere contained a series of concentric rings representing in order beginning with the outermost ring: the four quadrants of a circle each divided into ninety degrees; the signs of the zodiac divided into thirty degrees each; the days of the year, the circle being divided, for this purpose, into 365¼ equal parts; the names of the months, the number of days in each, and the small divisions which represent each day, which coincide exactly with those representing the days of the year; and lastly the saints' days, with their Sunday-letters. The purpose of the signs of the zodiac is to show the position of the sun in the ecliptic at different times. Therefore, if we find on the figure the fourth degree of Aries and the day of the month corresponding to it, we have the date March 16 as nearly as we can determine it by observing the intricate divisions in the figure.

The next passage "Noon hyer was he, whan she redy was" means evidently, 'he was no higher than this (i. e. four degrees) above the horizon when she was ready'; that is, it was a little past six. The method used in determining the time of day by observation of the sun's position is explained in the Astrolabe ii, 2 and 3. First the sun's altitude is found by means of the revolving rule at the back of the astrolabe. The rule, a piece of metal fitted with sights, is moved up and down until the rays of the sun shine directly through the sights. Then, by means of the degrees marked on the back of the astrolabe, the angle of elevation of the rule is determined, giving the altitude of the sun. The rest of the process involves the use of the *front* of the astrolabe. This side of the circular plate, shown in Fig. 2, had a thick rim with a wide depression in the middle. On the rim were three concentric circles, the first showing the letters A to Z, representing the twenty-four hours of the day, and the two innermost circles giving the degrees of the four quadrants. The depressed central part of the front was marked with three circles, the 'Tropicus Cancri', the 'AEquinoctialis,' and the 'Tropicus Capricorni'; and with the cross-lines from North to South, and from East to West. There were besides several thin plates or discs of metal of such a size as exactly to drop into the depression spoken of. The principal one of these was the 'Rete' and is shown in Fig. 2. "It consisted of a circular ring marked with the zodiacal signs, subdivided into degrees, with narrow branching limbs both within and without this ring, having smaller branches or tongues terminating in points, each of which denoted the exact position of some well-known star. * * * The 'Rete' being thus, as it were, a skeleton plate, allows the 'Tropicus Cancri,' etc., marked upon the body of the instrument, to be partially seen below it. * * * But it was more usual to interpose between the 'Rete' and the body of the instrument (called the 'Mother') another thin plate or disc, such as that in Fig. 5, so that portions of this latter plate could be seen beneath the skeleton-form of the 'Rete' (i. 17). These plates were called by Chaucer 'tables', and sometimes an instrument was provided with several of them, differently marked, for use in places having different latitudes. The one in Fig. 5 is suitable for the latitude of Oxford (nearly). The upper part, above the Horizon Obliquus, is marked with circles of altitude (i. 18), crossed by incomplete arcs of azimuth tending to a common centre, the zenith (i. 19)." [Skeat, *Introduction to the Astrolabe*, pp. lxxiv-lxxv.]

Now suppose we have taken the sun's altitude by §2 (Pt. ii of the *Astrolabe*) and found it to be 25½°. "As the altitude was taken by the *back* of the Astrolabe, turn it over, and then let the *Rete* revolve westward until the 1st point of Aries is just within the altitude-circle marked 25, allowing for the ½ degree by guess. This will bring the denticle near the letter C, and the first point of Aries near X, which means 9 a. m." [Skeat's note on the *Astrolabe* ii. 3, pp. 189-190].

IV. Chaucer would know the altitude of the sun simply by inspection of an astrolabe, without calculation. Skeat has explained this passage in his *Preface to Chaucer's Astrolabe* (E. E. T. S.), p. lxiii, as follows:

"Besides saying that the sun was 29° high, Chaucer says that his shadow was to his height in the proportion of 11 to 6. Changing this proportion, we can make it that of 12 to $6\frac{6}{11}$; that is, the point of the *Umbra Versa* (which is reckoned by twelfth parts) is $6\frac{6}{11}$ or 6½ nearly. (Umbra Recta and Umbra Versa were scales on the back of the astrolabe used for computing the altitudes of heavenly bodies from the height and shadows of objects. The *umbra recta* was used where the angle of elevation of an object was greater than 45°; the *umbra versa*, where it was less.) This can be verified by Fig. 1; for a straight edge, laid across from the 29th degree above the word 'Occidens,' and passing through the center, will cut the scale of Umbra Versa between the 6th and 7th points. The sun's altitude is thus established as 29° above the western horizon, beyond all doubt."

V. *Herberwe* means 'position.' Chaucer says here, then, that the sun according to his declination causing his position to be low or high in the heavens, brings about the seasons for all living things. In the *Astrolabe*, i. 17, there is a very interesting passage explaining in detail, declination, the solstices and equinoxes, and change of seasons. Chaucer is describing the front of the astrolabe. He says: "The plate under thy rite is descryved with 3 principal cercles; of whiche the leste is cleped the cercle of Cancer, by-cause that the heved of Cancer turneth evermor consentrik up-on the same cercle. (This corresponds to the Tropic of Cancer on the celestial sphere, which marks the greatest northern declination of the sun.) In this heved of Cancer is the grettest declinacioun northward of the sonne. And ther-for is he cleped the Solsticioun of Somer; whiche declinacioun, aftur Ptholome, is 23 degrees and 50 minutes, as wel in Cancer as in Capricorne. (The greatest declination of the sun measures the obliquity of the ecliptic, which is slightly variable. In Chaucer's time it was about 23° 31', and in the time of Ptolemy about 23° 40'. Ptolemy assigns it too high a value.) This signe of Cancre is cleped the Tropik of Somer, of *tropos*, that is to seyn 'agaynward'; for thanne by-ginneth the sonne to passe fro us-ward. (See Fig. 2 in Skeat's *Preface to the Astrolabe*, vol. iii, or E. E. T. S. vol. 16.)

The middel cercle in wydnesse, of thise 3, is cleped the Cercle Equinoxial (the celestial equator of the celestial sphere); up-on whiche turneth evermo the hedes of Aries and Libra. (These are the two signs in which the ecliptic crosses the equinoctial.) And understond wel, that evermo this Cercle Equinoxial turneth iustly fro verrey est to verrey west; as I have shewed thee in the spere solide. (As the earth rotates daily from west to east, the celestial sphere appears to us to revolve about the earth once every twenty-four hours from east to west. Chaucer, of course, means here that the equinoctial actually revolves with the *primum mobile* instead of only appearing to revolve.) This same cercle is cleped also the Weyere, *equator*, of the day; for whan the sonne is in the hevedes of Aries and Libra, than ben the dayes and the nightes ilyke of lengthe in al the world. And ther-fore ben thise two signes called Equinoxies.

The wydeste of thise three principal cercles is cleped the Cercle of Capricorne, by-cause that the heved of Capricorne turneth evermo consentrix up-on the same cercle. (That is to say, the Tropic of

Capricorn meets the ecliptic in the sign Capricornus, or, in other words, the sun attains its greatest declination southward when in the sign Capricornus.)   In the heved of this for-seide Capricorne is the grettest declinacioun southward of the sonne, and ther-for is it cleped the Solsticioun of Winter.   This signe of Capricorne is also cleped the Tropik of Winter, for thanne byginneth the sonne to come agayn to us-ward."

VI.   The moon's orbit around the earth is inclined at an angle of about 5° to the earth's orbit around the sun.   The moon, therefore, appears to an observer on the earth as if traversing a great circle of the celestial sphere just as the sun appears to do; and the moon's real orbit projected against the celestial sphere appears as a great circle similar to the ecliptic.   This great circle in which the moon appears to travel will, therefore, be inclined to the ecliptic at an angle of 5° and the moon will appear in its motion never far from the ecliptic; it will always be within the zodiac which extends eight or nine degrees on either side of the ecliptic.

The angular velocity of the moon's motion in its projected great circle is much greater than that of the sun in the ecliptic.   Both bodies appear to move in the same direction, from west to east; but the solar apparent revolution takes about a year averaging 1° daily, while the moon completes a revolution from any fixed star back to the same star in about 27¼ days, making an average daily angular motion of about 13°.   The actual daily angular motion of the moon varies considerably; hence in trying to test out Chaucer's references to lunar angular velocity it would not be correct to make use only of the average angular velocity since his references apply to specific times and therefore the variation in the moon's angular velocity must be taken into account.

VII.   On the line "In two of Taur," etc., Skeat has the following note: "Tyrwhitt unluckily altered *two* to *ten*, on the plea that 'the time (*four days complete*, l. 1893) is not sufficient for the moon to pass from the second degree of Taurus into Cancer.'   And he then proceeds to shew this, taking the *mean* daily motion of the moon as being 13 degrees, 10 minutes, and 35 seconds.   But, as Mr. Brae has shewn, in his edition of Chaucer's Astrolabe, p. 93, footnote, it is a mistake to reckon here the moon's *mean* motion; we must rather consider her *actual* motion.   The question is simply, can the moon move from the 2nd degree of Taurus to the 1st of Cancer (through 59 degrees) in four days?   Mr. Brae says decidedly, that examples of such motion are to be seen 'in every almanac.'

For example, in the Nautical Almanac, in June, 1886, the moon's longitude at noon was 30° 22' on the 9th, and 90° 17' on the 13th; i. e., the moon was in the *first* of Taurus on the former day, and in the *first* of Cancer on the latter day, at the same hour; which gives (very nearly) a degree more of change of longitude than we here require. The MSS all have *two* or *tuo*, and they are quite right. The motion of the moon is so variable that the mean motion affords no safe guide." [Skeat, *Notes to the Canterbury Tales*, p. 363.]

VIII. The moon's "waxing and waning" is due to the fact that the moon is not self-luminous but receives its light from the sun and to the additional fact that it makes a complete revolution around the earth with reference to the sun in 29½ days. When the earth is on the side of the moon that faces the sun we see the full moon, that is, the whole illuminated hemisphere. But when we are on the side of the moon that is turned away from the sun we face its unilluminated hemisphere and we say that we have a 'new moon.' Once in every 29½ days the earth is in each of these positions with reference to the moon and, of course, in the interval of time between these two phases we are so placed as to see larger or smaller parts of the illuminating hemisphere of the moon, giving rise to the other visible phases.

When the moon is between the earth and the sun she is said to be in *conjunction*, and is invisible to us for a few nights. This is the phase called *new moon*. As she emerges from conjunction we see the moon as a delicate crescent in the west just after sunset and she soon sets below the horizon. Half of the moon's surface is illuminated, but we can see only a slender edge with the horns turned away from the sun. The crescent appears a little wider each night, and, as the moon recedes 13° further from the sun each night, she sets correspondingly later, until in her first quarter half of the illuminated hemisphere is turned toward us. As the moon continues her progress around the earth she gradually becomes gibbous and finally reaches a point in the heavens directly opposite the sun when she is said to be in *opposition*, her whole illumined hemisphere faces us and we have *full moon*. She then rises in the east as the sun sets in the west and is on the meridian at midnight. As the moon passes from opposition, the portion of her illuminated hemisphere visible to us gradually decreases, she rises nearly an hour later each evening and in the morning is seen high in the western sky after sunrise. At her *third quarter* she again presents half of her illuminated surface to us and continues to decrease until we see her in crescent form again. But now her position with reference to the sun is exactly the reverse of her position as a waxing crescent, so that her horns are now turned toward the west away from the sun, and she appears in the eastern sky just before sunrise. The moon again comes into conjunction and is lost in the sun's rays and from this point the whole process is repeated.

IX. That the apparent motions of the sun and moon are not so complicated as those of the planets will be clear at once if we remember that the sun's apparent motion is caused by our seeing the sun projected against the celestial sphere in the ecliptic, the path cut out by the plane of the earth's orbit, while in the case of the moon, what we see is the moon's actual motion around the earth projected against the celestial sphere in the great circle traced by the moon's own orbital plane produced to an indefinite extent. These motions are further complicated by the rotation of the earth on its own axis, causing the rising and setting of the sun and the moon. These two bodies, however, always appear to be moving directly on in their courses, each completing a revolution around the earth in a definite time, the sun in a year, the moon in 29½ days. What we see in the case of the planets, on the other hand, is a complex motion compounded of the effects of the earth's daily rotation, its yearly revolution around the sun, and the planets' own revolutions in different periods of time in elliptical orbits around the sun. These complex planetary motions are characterized by the peculiar oscillations known as 'direct' and 'retrograde' movements.

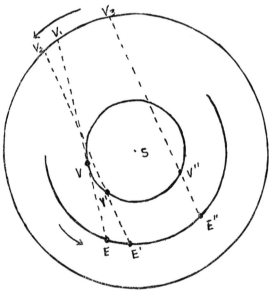

Fig. 4.

The motion of a planet is said to be *direct* when it moves in the direction of the succession of the zodiacal signs; *retrograde* when in the contrary direction. All of the planets have periods of retrograde and direct motion, though their usual direction is direct, from west to east. Retrograde motion can be explained by reference to the accompanying diagrams. In Fig. 4, the outer circle represents the path of the zodiac on the celestial sphere. Let the two inner circles represent the orbits of the earth and an inferior planet, Venus, around the sun, at S. (An *inferior* planet is one whose orbit around the sun is within that of the earth. A *superior* planet is one whose orbit is outside that of the earth.) V, V' and V", and E, E', and E" are successive positions of the two planets in their orbits, the arc VV" being longer than the arc EE" because the nearer a planet is to the

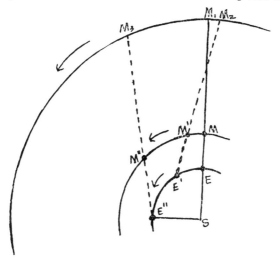

Fig. 5.

sun, the greater is its velocity. Then when Venus is at V and the earth at E, we shall see Venus projected on the celestial sphere at V₁. When Venus has passed on to V' the earth will have passed to E' and we shall see Venus on the celestial sphere at V₂. The apparent motion of the planet thus far will have been direct, from west to east in the order of the signs. But when Venus is at V" and the earth at E" Venus will be seen at V₃ having apparently moved back about two signs in a direction the reverse of that taken at first. This is called the planet's retrograde motion. At some point beyond V", the planet will appear to stop moving for a very short period and then resume its direct motion. In Fig. 5, the outer arc again represents the path of the zodiac on the celestial sphere. The smaller arcs represent the orbits of the superior planet, Mars, and the earth around the sun, S. At the point of opposition of Mars (when Mars and the sun are at opposite points in the heavens to an observer on the earth) we should see Mars projected on the zodiac at M_1. After a month Mars will be at M' and the earth at E', so that in its apparent motion Mars will have retrograded to M_2. After three months from opposition Mars will be at M'' and the earth at E'', making Mars appear at M_3 on the celestial sphere, its motion having changed from retrograde to direct.

Both Figures 4 and 5 take no account of the fact that the earth's orbit and those of the planets are not in exactly the same planes. Remembering this fact we see at once that the apparent oscillations of the planets are not back and forth in a straight line but in curves and spirals. It is easy to see why the apparent motions of the planets were accounted for by deferents and epicycles, before the Copernican system revealed the true nature of the solar system as heliocentric and not geocentric.

SELECTED BIBLIOGRAPHY

BERRY, ARTHUR, *A Short History of Astronomy.* New York. 1899.

BRYANT, W. W., *A History of Astronomy.* London. 1907.

CUMONT, FRANZ, *Astrology and Religion among the Greeks and Romans.* New York. 1912.

CUSHMAN, H. E., *A Beginner's History of Philosophy.* Boston. 1910.

DREYER, J. L. E., *History of the Planetary Systems from Thales to Kepler.* Cambridge. 1906.

EVERSHED, M. A., *Dante and the Early Astronomers.* London. 1913.

GOMPERZ, T., *Greek Thinkers, A History of Ancient Philosophy.* New York. 1901.

GORE J. ELLARD, *Astronomical Essays, Historical and Descriptive.* London. 1907.

HINKS, A. R., *Astronomy.* London. 1911.

JACOBY, HAROLD, *Astronomy.* New York. 1913.

IASTROW, MORRIS, "Astrology," *Encyclopaedia Britannica* ii, 795-800.

LEA, H. C., *History of the Inquisition of the Middle Ages.* New York. 1906. III. 409-549.

ORCHARD, T. N., *Milton's Astronomy.* New York. 1913.

TAYLOR, H. O., *The Mediaeval Mind.* 2 vols. New York. 1911.

TODD, MABEL L., *Steele's Popular Astronomy.* New York. 1884.

TRAILL, H. D., *Social England.* New York and London. 1902.

WALLACE, A. R., *Man's Place in the Universe.* London. 1903.

WHITE, A. D., *Warfare of Science with Theology.* New York and London. 1909. I. 381.

CHAUCER, *The Complete Works of Geoffrey Chaucer.* W. W. Skeat, edit. Clarendon Press. 1894.

CHAUCER, *Treatise on the Astrolabe,* A. E. Brae, edit. London. 1870.

Cambridge History of English Literature, The, ed. by A. W. Ward and A. R. Waller. Vol. II. 1908.

TEN BRINK, BERNARD, *History of English Literature.* Vol. II. New York. 1893.

COURTHOPE, W. J., *Literary History of the English People.* Vol. I. New York. 1898.

HADOW, GRACE E., *Chaucer and His Times.* New York. 1914.

HAMMOND, ELEANOR P., *Chaucer: A Bibliographical Manual.* New York. 1908.

JUSSERAND, J. J., *History of English Poetry.* Vol. II. London. 1895.

KITTREDGE, G. L., *Chaucer and His Poetry.* Harvard University Press. 1915.

LEGOUIS, EMILE, *Geoffrey Chaucer.* Trans. by L. Lailavoix. London. 1913.

LOUNSBURY, T. R., *Studies in Chaucer.* New York. 1892.

MORLEY, HENRY, *English Writers.* Vol. V. London. 1887 ff.

ROOT, ROBERT K., *The Poetry of Chaucer.* Boston and New York. 1906.

TATLOCK, JOHN S. P., "Astrology and Magic in Chaucer's *Franklin's Tale.*" Kittredge Anniversary Papers. 1913.

TATLOCK, JOHN S. P., *The Scene of the Franklin's Tale Visited.* Chaucer Society Publications. 1914.